# VILLAGE PRA

BEWARE THE BULL
G.Younger

# VILLAGE PRACTICE

*A Year in the Life of a Country Doctor's Wife*

Anne Stratford

Illustrations by Gill Younger

EX LIBRIS PRESS

First published in 1996 by
EX LIBRIS PRESS
1 The Shambles
Bradford on Avon
Wiltshire

Design and typesetting by Ex Libris Press

Cover printed by Shires Press
Trowbidge, Wiltshire
Printed and bound Cromwell Press
Broughton Gifford, Wiltshire

Set in 10 point Times



ISBN 0 948578 78 5

# *Village Initiation*

I HAD JUST STARTED TO unpack another tea chest when the door bell began to peal as if someone was leaning against it.

"I'm coming," I shouted as I clattered down our uncarpeted cottage stairs. The shadowy figure seen through the glass continued to ring the bell as I unlatched the door. The ringing stopped abruptly as the man, deprived of the support of the door, crumpled inwards. I jumped back as he occupied most of the space at the foot of the stairs.

"Is he dead?" my small son James asked with interest from the third stair. His sister Clare watched pop-eyed, thumb in mouth, from the safety of the half-landing.

The figure at my feet gave a convulsive snore.

"No he's alive," I said with relief. "Get some blankets."

"If we can find any," James said with all the scorn of a five-year-old faced with adult thoughtlessness. "You haven't made us proper beds yet. We've been camping since we got here."

"Blankets piled on the spare bed," I tried to sound calm as I examined my first patient. The diagnosis was not difficult. As I bent over him I was almost knocked backwards by the fumes of alcohol. Years of experience in hospitals had taught me to recognise the smells of beer and spirits, even meths, but this was different – a sweeter smell. Then I remembered where I was. I sat back on my heels; we had just moved to cider country.

That morning my husband Peter had put on his new suit and left the cottage to do his first surgery in the village where he was to be the only doctor. The suit had been a major investment – twenty-pounds worth of thorn-proof tweed. When he put it on Peter aged ten years.

"How do I look?" he asked anxiously straightening his college tie.

I resisted the temptation to tell him that he looked like a medical student dressed as a country GP for a university pantomime.

"Very rural," I said, "pull your stethoscope up so that it shows in your pocket and you look just the part." I glanced down at my own dusty jeans,

"I'm not dressed as the country doctor's wife am I?"

"No one will expect you to appear in a twin set and pearls, this is 1974 not 1954." Peter smoothed his unruly black hair and picked up his very new doctor's bag.

"Right then," he smiled at the children who were both busy with dishes of breakfast cereal. "Bye you two, see you later. Be good and help Mummy with the unpacking." He turned to me, "right then," he said again more nervously, "this is it."

"Good luck, Doctor Stratford," I gave Peter a gentle push towards the door.

He stopped in the doorway. "Don't forget that the telephone will be put through to the extension here at half past ten when the receptionist goes home. You must be here."

"I'll be here," I said reassuringly not really understanding that my life was to be ruled by the telephone from then on.

The cold, late spring rain which had greeted us on our arrival in the village was still falling as Peter dashed out to the car parked at the side of the cottage. A heap of builder's rubble was piled where we hoped to build a garage. I stood for a moment in the doorway waving as Peter drove down the lane. Before I turned back to tackle the chores and more unpacking I looked at the rubble. If only, I thought, we could have bought the cottage before the builder had 'renovated' it we could have prevented his wholesale removal of the original fireplaces, old windows and flagstones now heaped outside. But we had been too short of time and cash when Peter was appointed to the practice to look further than Brook Cottage which was empty and cheap. The builder had already replaced flagstoned floors with lino tiles of a lurid orange colour and built a 'feature' fireplace with stone from the old pantry walls. The pantry would have been useful, the fireplace was not. It not only looked wrong but it smoked. With a sigh I shut out the rain and went into the kitchen to clear away breakfast before making a start on unpacking the rest of the boxes upstairs. I had just succeeded in unpacking all the children's toys and clothes when the ringing doorbell announced that I had started work as the village doctor's wife.

While the children looked for a blanket I phoned through to the surgery. Our elderly receptionist clearly thought that I was telephoning to ask Peter to come home to fix some domestic appliance until I explained that I had an unconscious patient on the floor at my feet. Almost reluctantly she agreed to send for an ambulance. I felt that the doctors' wives she had known before would have dealt with the problem single-handed.

"He's leaking," James told me laconically as he handed me the blanket. I had hoped he wouldn't notice the growing puddle on the hall floor. For the first time I was glad of the dreadful orange lino tiles. The fitted carpet I coveted might never have recovered from recycled cider.

"An ambulance is coming so why don't you and Clare go and watch for it and tell me when it arrives?" I said too brightly.

James gave me a pitying look, "you'll hear it, they make a very loud noise you know." Children always know when adults are trying to get rid of them but James and Clare could not resist climbing into the deep window-sill to kneel and watch for the ambulance to appear in the lane.

"It's here," James yelled suddenly after about fifteen minutes. "He isn't making a noise," he added in disappointed tones, "he's flashing his blue light though."

I climbed over my patient to open the front door as the ambulance backed alongside the front wall of the cottage. One navy-uniformed man came towards me as the other opened up the rear doors of the ambulance.

"Good morning, we got a call from the surgery, you got a patient here have you?" he peered over my shoulder. "Oh it's Bert is it." He gave me a reassuring smile, "you the new doctor's wife are you?" I saw his eyes take in my grubby jeans and I realised that I was not making the same impression as I once did in a nurse's uniform and frilly cap.

"It's only Bert, Fred, " he called over his shoulder to his colleague who was getting a stretcher out of the ambulance. The other man's lugubrious expression hardly changed.

"Good job we didn't bother with the siren then."

"You'll see a fair bit of old Bert I expect from now on," the first man bent down to inspect the patient. "Diabetic Bert is and too fond of the cider. Hello you two," he caught sight of the children who had retreated to the top step of the stairs. With swift efficiency the two men loaded Bert onto their stretcher and into the ambulance. As Fred closed the big rear doors I suddenly felt left out. I wanted to go with the patient. I wanted to return to the world I knew, the safe hospital world where doctors, nurses and other staff share the responsibility for patients. The enormity of what Peter and I had taken on swept over me as I stood on the doorstep and watched the heavy ambulance lurch away down the lane. I took a deep breath. Beyond the garden the trees in the cider orchard had decorated their gnarled old branches with apple blossom; I had been too busy since our arrival to notice.

"Mrs Stratford. Excuse me." Through the rain I saw a figure lean over the crumbling stone wall which separated our garden from the lane. An elderly man held out a bunch of flowers. I clambered over the heap of builder's rubble to accept them.

"I couldn't help seeing the ambulance, I do hope it isn't serious," the man's expression was anxious. "We've been away you see or we would have called before. Earnest and May Hayward of Cowslip Cottage." He offered the flowers, a mixed bunch of spring garden flowers – polyanthus, auricula, hellebores and daphne. I took the flowers and held the damp bunch to my nose. After the smell of fermented cider they were welcome as a judge's nosegay.

"Thank you, Mr Hayward, these are lovely. The ambulance was for a patient and not I think too serious." His anxious expression relaxed and his face lit up as he caught sight of the children peering out of the front door. "My wife is baking ginger biscuits," he whispered, "would the children be allowed gingerbread men if we were to make some?"

"They would indeed, Mr Hayward," I said and knew then that however difficult life was going to be as the wife of a village doctor there would be compensations.

"Tea at four o'clock then?"

"Thank you, we will look forward to that."

At lunch time Peter arrived home and before I could enquire about his first surgery or even tell him about my own patient, he rushed past me taking the stairs two at a time. I shrugged and got on with serving the lunch.

"Daddy, why have you taken your trousers off?" James's question almost made me drop the salad bowl I was removing from the fridge. I stood up and turned to see Peter at the kitchen door in shirt and socks.

"Now I really know how the saints must have felt," he groaned as he sat at the table.

Puzzled, I set out the plates, "surgery was that bad?"

"No, the patients were fine, it's that tweed suit, it's like a hair shirt. I could hardly sit still to listen to the patients symptoms I was so uncomfortable. Look … " Peter displayed the red angry looking rash on his hairy legs. The children giggled.

"But it cost so much money," I began.

"I don't care how much it cost," Peter said with feeling as he helped himself to salad, "from now on that suit stays in the wardrobe. I wont even need to hang the damn thing up, it's practically self-supporting."

I found a bottle of calamine lotion which Peter used to anoint his spots. He ate lunch as his legs turned a dusty shade of pink.

"I'm off to do my visits then," he announced when he came back downstairs later in his old trousers and elbow-patched jacket. "Here's the list of patients," he held out a list written in the receptionist's schoolgirl-neat hand. "Don't ring me unless it is really urgent."

I looked at him over my shoulder from the sink where I was washing up. "I think three years as a staff nurse on night duty taught me when *not* to call a doctor."

Peter grinned, "Not like old Coitus Interruptus."

"Peter!" I grimaced at him, jerking my head in the direction of the children who were still scraping the last of the pudding from their plates.

"Well that was what we all called night sister in the doctor's mess."

"Well you aren't in the doctor's mess now," I dried my hands and took the list. "OK, off you go, Dr Kildare. I'll cope. Oh, by the way we are going to Cowslip Cottage for tea later."

"Not until Joan comes back to take the phone."

"No, I haven't forgotten. We can't go out until she arrives to do surgery at four and we have to be back here to take over again by half past six or you will turn us all into pumpkins." The children giggled again.

"Bye hairy legs," James called cheekily but Peter had already gone.

When the lunch was cleared away and I was ready to start unpacking another box the doorbell rang again. This time I opened it slowly.

"Mrs Stratford? How do you do. Polkinhorne." The man on the doorstep wore one of the brown shopkeeper's overalls I hadn't seen since 1955. He attempted a smile and displayed a row of broken tombstone teeth. "I have come," he went on, "to solicit your esteemed custom."

For a moment I was lost for words. Where we had come from in London there was only one sort of soliciting and somehow he did not look the type. Then I saw his bike propped against the cottage wall. The heavy old frame supported a delivery boy's basket at the front.

"My shop is in the village square. I regret I can't deliver any more. I can't get boys." Mr Polkinhorne wrung his hands like a hungry giant.

"Thank you, Mr Polkinhorne." I smiled with relief as I realised that he only wanted to sell me groceries. "I will come and do some shopping just as soon as I can."

I watched him wobble away up the lane on his old bike. Later the telephone began to ring again.

"Dr Stratford's house," I said feeling foolish.

"Is that the doctor's? " The voice was very aged and cracked. "Tell him to come quick, I'm dying."

I scrabbled about among the envelopes and lists on the hall table for a pen. "Give me your name and address," I shouted down the telephone.

"I can't, I told you I'm dying. I'm all alone. My wicked daughter has gone out and left me all alone again and I'm going." The voice faded and I clutched the receiver. Clare chose that moment to set up a wailing cry of, "I want to talk on the telephone."

Frantically I motioned to James to remove his sister but she did not want to be removed. Something interesting was happening and she wanted to be in on the action. I put my hand over the receiver, "get her toy telephone, quickly," I hissed at James. With a look of complete disgust on his face James went to fetch Clare's plastic toy telephone from upstairs.

"Now please try to tell me your name and address so that I can tell my husband how to find you," I pleaded with my caller who responded by wailing again, "I'm, dying, I'm dying," then the line went dead. I stared at the receiver in my hand for a moment before replacing it and wondered what to do. Should I get the call traced? I pictured the slumped body at the other end. I jumped as the telephone rang again but this time, not the ringing of an incoming call but the noise of the intercom from the surgery. I snatched the receiver. "Joan?"

"Yes, Mrs Stratford, I am back on duty. You can leave the telephone to me now until evening surgery is over."

"But I've just had an emergency call and the patient didn't have time to tell me her name or give any information and she's dying." My throat was so dry that my voice gave out on a croak.

"Oh that's all right, Mrs Stratford, don't worry," Joan's voice was extraordinarily calm. "That would be Mrs Pringle. She telephones every day when her daughter goes out to do her shopping. She hates being left alone."

"But she said she was dying," I croaked.

"That's right, that is what she always says. Dr Thomas used to call her Mrs I'm Dying. In rather poor taste I always thought. One day the poor woman will die. But don't you worry, I will telephone her neighbour Mrs Cox. She usually looks in on these occasions and gives her a cup of tea until Mary comes home again."

I leaned weakly against the wall. "You mean these calls happen frequently?"

"All the time."

"And it's a hoax?"

"Oh no," Joan sounded shocked. "Poor Mrs Pringle, she just wants some attention."

I knew how she felt. "Thank you, Joan. You'll take over then?"

"Certainly."

I replaced the receiver and looked at the telephone with huge relief. For two hours it was not going to be my job to answer it or deal with the next batch of problems.

"Come on you two," I called up the stairs, "we can go out now."

Clare appeared clutching her toy telephone. James pushed past her on the stairs and made for the door like an escaping prisoner. I caught his arm, "hang on, wait for your sister," I took the plastic telephone and put it beside the real one. "There you are," I said to Clare, "neither of us has to answer our phones for two whole hours now."

Clare stopped sucking her thumb and said hopefully, "pick up?"

"No, you can walk, we aren't going far and I think there might be a treat at the end."

After that it was easy. I locked the cottage and we set off down the lane. The sun had come out for the first time since our arrival in the village. A pair of noisy starlings were taking sunlit showers in a deep puddle by our gate.

I chose the long way round to our neighbour's cottage. We passed pairs of identical cottages with gardens as unlike as they could be. The first garden was as neat as a sampler stitched with rows of seedlings and new plants, the next door garden was decorated with rhubarb flowers and the yellow flowers of last year's brassicas gone to seed. We turned down one of the high walled footpaths which ran behind the cottages.

"I like this," Clare whispered, "it's magic."

I knew what she meant. We were so used to streets with curbs and cars, traffic fumes and buses. This high-walled path was safe. Real wallflowers grew in the loose mortared wall above our heads. We passed gates to unseen gardens. Ammonites – big curled fossils – had been used to add a flourish to the courses of field stone used to build the wall. The children kept finding smaller fossils in the limestone. Our progress was slow.

We found Cowslip Cottage where the lane opened out into the part of the village called South End.

"Come in, come in," Mr Hayward greeted us with genuine pleasure, "come through and meet my wife." He took us through to a lean-to conservatory. Plants stood in every possible space, a door was open to the garden.

Mrs Hayward, who had a face like a happy gargoyle, came in with a tray of tea things. Reluctantly I stopped admiring the plants and watched my children with a wary eye. I need not have worried. Mrs Hayward offered them both a perfectly formed gingerbread man. "There you are my dears, off you go into the garden with them. Go and see the calves."

James immediately bit the head off his gingerbread man and shot out into the garden. Clare followed eating currant buttons.

"There now, you can sit down in peace for a moment my dear." Mrs Hayward plumped up a cushion for me and handed me a cup of tea. I sank gratefully into a faded old chair with a view of the garden and the orchard beyond. Under the apple trees, young heifers stood knee deep in buttercups swinging their tasselled tails. James and Clare had scrambled onto the low garden wall and were happily watching the calves and cannibalising their gingerbread men.

"This is bliss," I sighed as I relaxed and drank fragrant tea, the air from the garden and the scent of pot plants washing over me.

"Moving house must be very wearing," said Mrs Hayward, "I have never tried it but I can imagine."

"My wife was born in this cottage," Mr Hayward explained, "we were engaged to be married for twenty years while she cared for her parents. When they died we were married over there." He nodded towards the church tower, visible over the orchard trees.

"That's why we have no children," Mrs Hayward glanced outside at Clare and James, "we left it too late you see. A biscuit my dear?"

"Thank you," I said, helping myself to a home-made biscuit, "moving is hard work but I feel we are going to be very happy here."

"You will find this a friendly village," Mr Hayward leaned back in his chair, "but be warned, they will all know who you are and will expect you to know who they are. Even more important is to know to whom they are related. I'm not a native as my wife is and it took me a very long time to sort them all out in my mind. I still haven't untangled all the relationships, what with bicycle grandfathers and … ”

“Ernest, what will the doctor’s wife think of you!”

“Bicycle grandfathers?” I was intrigued.

Mrs Hayward glanced outside to make sure that the children were out of earshot. “Before we had a bus service and before so many people had cars, most lads found girl friends within the village but those who owned bicycles sometimes sowed their wild oats further afield. So you can’t always tell who is related to whom.”

I felt as if I had walked into the world of village England between the wars. When the clock on the church tower chimed the half hour I could have relaxed in that quiet conservatory for a whole afternoon.

“I met Mr Polkinhorne earlier,” I said as I accepted another cup of tea. “I promised to visit his shop. I do need a few things.”

“Well look carefully before you buy. Bill’s goods are not always as fresh as they should be,” Mrs Hayward warned. She looked at the clock. “If you want to walk up to the shop without the children they are more than welcome to stay here if you think they would stay with strangers.”

“Oh I’m sure they would. What a kind thought. I will take you up on that.” When I drained my tea I stood up, “if you are quite sure … ?”

“Quite sure.” Mrs Hayward walked out into the garden, “children, your mother is going to do some shopping. Would you like to stay here? Mr Hayward will be feeding the hens shortly and you can help him.”

I half expected protests, from Clare if not from James, but they had lost all interest in me. Clearly I could not compete against hens.

Mr Polkinhorne’s shop was one of the row of buildings which propped each other up in the High Street. Inside, it smelled of old vegetables. An attempt had been made to turn the shop into something like a mini-market. Two rooms had been thrown together with shelving around the sides and a tall island unit in the centre. At one end Mr Polkinhorne stood behind an old wooden counter on which stood a baker’s tray of pies and a large cheese. A pile of tattered wicker shopping baskets did duty for wire ones. As I began to walk around the shelves I could hear a conversation on the other side of the centre unit.

“He ’ent no bloody good. I told him I’d got a stoppage and my bum do pain I cruel but he weren’t listening to I.”

“Didn’t ’un give ’ee none of that gunpowder jallop old Doctor Thomas used to dole out?”

"He wouldn't give I nothing."

I realised with horror that I was overhearing patients talking about Peter. I froze beside the breakfast cereals.

"Do 'ee know what he told I to eat, Stan? Bran! I told him, Doctor I says, when I was a lad us fed Bran to the horses and now us d'give Bran to the chickens. I "ent no horse nor no chicken and I wants a perscripshun to shift I."

"Did 'un give 'ee one, Walt?"

"No 'ee bloody didn't. Just kept telling I to eat brown bread and bran. Pah!"

I heard feet shuffling towards the counter so I moved further around the end of the island unit. From there I could see the two old men now leaning over Mr Polkinhorne's counter.

"I'll have a loaf of Mothers Sorrow, if you've got one put by for me, Bill," Walt said, "and some of they Bile Beans. They'll shift I."

Mr Polkinhorne leaned over the counter and whispered to the two old men. They turned and stared at me. I reached up to take a packet from the nearest shelf to cover my confusion. I could not remain in hiding while taking advantage of Mrs Hayward's kindness. I had to face the two old men who still propped up the counter when I had filled my basket.

"Afternoon." Walt with the stoppage gave me a steady stare and then looked in my basket. "You don't feed them dried fish pellets to the doctor do you? I thought he'd live on Bran."

Confused I looked in my basket and found that I had picked up a packet of dried cat food instead of muesli. The two old men cackled at the joke.

I smiled weakly, I'll have one of those pork pies please, Mr Polkinhorne."

"Oho, living dangerously that is." Walt said, "Bill's pies is not health food, not health food at all."

Still chortling they moved to leave the shop as another man entered. I blinked, he was the double of the patient who had fallen through my front door that morning.

"How's Bert then, Alf," Stan asked as they met in the shop doorway. "I heard they'd taken 'un up th' hospital."

Alf nodded. "His sugar diabetes is playing him up again. I've got to catch the next bus to get up there to see him."

"Come to buy some grapes for your brother then?" The three old men enjoyed this joke at Mr Polkinhorne's expense. The only fruit visible were some withered apples and oranges.

Alf gave a cheerless smile, "Bert's usual please, Mr P., before the bus comes."

Mr Polkinhorne reached under the counter to extract an oversized bottle. "Excuse me a moment, Mrs Stratford. I'll put it on his bill will I Alf?"

Alf nodded and grasped the huge whisky bottle by the neck and left the shop with the two old men just as the village bus drew up outside.

Mr Polkinhorne leaned across the counter and said, "don't worry, Mrs Stratford, that bottle was not full of whisky."

"Thank goodness for that. There would have been enough in that bottle to make a whole ward full of patients drunk."

"Oh dear me no, it is nothing like that at all. Just Bert's favourite. I get it from the farm for him. He provides the empty bottle for me to fill.

"From the farm?"

"Cider, Mrs Stratford, scrumpy, farm cider you know. Lovely local cider, perfectly harmless I can assure you."

Speechless, I paid for my goods. As I walked back to collect the children I felt a sympathy for the unknown ward staff who were soon going to have both Alf and Bert to cope with. The children were reluctant to leave Cowslip Cottage. They were only persuaded by Mrs Hayward giving them each two bantam's eggs to take home for their tea.

After the eggs were cooked and eaten, the children were bathed and put to bed before Peter arrived home. He looked exhausted.

"I'm starving, we were so busy I never even had a cup of tea. What's for supper?"

I thought guiltily of my pleasant afternoon tea in Cowslip cottage conservatory. "I've bought some local things to try." I put the baker's pie on the table and cut into it.

Peter peered at his piece of pie, "well if I run short of penicillin I shall know where to go for a supply."

I looked down. The inside of the pork pie was green. I turned to the wedge of cheese I had bought in the village shop. "Let's try this then." I unwrapped the wedge of cheese. It displayed a perfect set of Mr Polkinhorne's finger prints.

"Just scrape them off," Peter suggested wearily. "They wont kill us."

He munched the cheese with a hunk of fresh bread. "Umm not bad, tastes like real cheese instead of that plastic stuff you used to buy in supermarkets."

He looked at the cheese speculatively, "just think, most of this stuff is made by my patients."

"Is that a recommendation?"

"Ask me again in a few years," Peter said as the telephone began to ring. He went into the hall and I heard a familiar voice echoing down the phone.

"I'm dying, come quickly."

I went out to the hall and tried to attract Peter's attention but he flapped a hand at me to go away. "What address is it," he shouted down the phone.

"Mummy. Daddy woke me up," a voice from the stairs wailed and I looked up to see Clare in pyjamas clutching her cuddling blanket.

"She's put the phone down," Peter said staring at me, "it's an old lady who says she's dying and I don't know who she is or where she is."

"That's what I was trying to tell you. Her name is Mrs Pringle and she rings up every day. Didn't Joan tell you about her? I had her on the phone this afternoon. She just rings up when her middle-aged daughter goes out and she feels the need of attention."

"But we cant be sure of that." Peter ran his fingers through his hair.

"Mummy," Clare wailed from the top of the stairs. Then the doorbell rang.

"Now what?" Peter pulled the door open and I saw Walt with the stoppage on the doorstep.

He held something out to me. "Since you got them dried pellets I thought you'd better have 'ee for the mice." He thrust a half-grown cat into my arms. "Tell 'ee what, doctor Bile Beans works, you can keep your Bran. Good evening."

The cat sank its claws into my arm and I dropped him on the floor.

Clare flew downstairs and began to croon over the cat.

"Mummy, he's made a puddle."

I looked down to see the cat's puddle spreading over the same patch of floor that my morning patient had watered too.

Peter and I looked at each other and then we began to laugh.

Do adolescent cats drink cider around here?" I gasped.

I wouldn't be surprised at anything they do round here,' replied Peter with feeling.

❦

# *Dogs and Dinner Parties*

OUR FIRST WEEKEND ON DUTY began quite peacefully. Peter did Saturday morning surgery while I rushed to the bakers and the butchers and did everything in the village which would be out of bounds to me until Joan returned on Monday morning to take over the telephone.

"I think we could tackle the pile of rubble," Peter said staring out of the kitchen window at lunch time. "I'll pull an old boiler suit on so that I can do a quick transformation job if I get an emergency call."

It was the first really warm weekend of the year. I worked outside in a T-shirt and shorts and the children quickly abandoned similar outfits and demanded that we fill the galvanised bath we had found in the garden shed. While Peter started shifting stone I went to the shed to get the bath.

The shed was a tumble-down stone building, with a collapsing tiled roof. Behind the wash copper in the corner I had found old photographs of wedding groups in 1920's clothes. Staring out at me through broken glass was the bride who had probably spent years stirring the family wash in the old copper. On the remains of a coal heap in a corner were pokers, hearth brushes and a chestnut roaster old enough for us to regard them as antiques. Garden tools with riveted handles were propped in a corner where the galvanised bath hung from a hook on the wall. I unhooked the bath and carried it to the tiny lawn in front of the cottage, almost the only bit of garden that the builder had not used as a rubbish dump. An inch or two of water delighted the children and allowed me to join Peter who had been stone shifting for half an hour. He groaned as he straightened his back.

"This is like dismantling the pyramids."

"Don't exaggerate, that's my role." I peered over the low side wall to where an obliging local farmer had parked a trailer. He wanted hard-core to fill in his muddy gateways and we wanted rid of the rubble we had inherited from the builder.

"Percy Coombes will be back for the trailer at five o'clock," Peter said wincing as he massaged his back. "I'm not sure that's a good idea, I think I should have said Monday morning. I've been heaving stone for ages and look at it – I haven't even covered the floor of the trailer yet." He looked at me enviously. "I might do better if I could strip off. I'm boiled in this boiler suit."

I ignored his dreadful joke and looked at him speculatively. "I wonder how long it takes firemen to get their pyjamas off and their uniforms on when the fire-bell goes?"

"Dunno," Peter grunted as he began sorting and heaving stones over the wall again. "What do you suggest, a greasy pole from our bedroom window to the car?"

"No, just clean trousers and an open-necked shirt ready in the kitchen and your jacket and bag ready in the car."

Peter gave me one of those looks men give when you've had an idea which they didn't think of first. He clambered down from the stone heap and disappeared into the house. I went on throwing stones into the trailer.

"You don't want to get rid of all they stones." A voice from over the wall made me jump. I had narrowly avoided giving Peter his first surgical emergency by heaving a rock at old Walt's head

"These walls is delapicated. You need the good stone to mend 'ee. Look." Old Walt pulled a stone out of the garden wall and brought a shower of stone and dry mortar out with it. "He'll be down one winter, I know, my Dad were a stonemason."

"Which stones would be useful for wall repairs then Mr Er?"

"The name's Walter Ford." His face split into a grin and he leaned on his stick and peered over the wall at my bare legs. "I come 'cos they told I up the village you was nude sunbathin' down here." Walt sounded disappointed.

James and Clare chose that moment to leap out of the old bath and chase each other naked round the lawn. Peter reappeared wearing only old shorts.

"Afternoon, Doctor. I was just tellin' your Missus here you don't want to get shot of all this good stone. You give old Percy Coombes the rubbish for his gates but you want to keep the building stone for your walls. Cost you good money to buy more in."

Peter nodded as if he had already considered the important matter of building stone. "I have started keeping some back," he said, indicating the small pile he had grudgingly allowed me to keep for the rockery I planned.

"That's no good. You wants stones like these." Walt reached up to the trailer, picked up a stone, weighed it in his hand and threw it back over the wall. "This is a good one too," he threw back another. By the time he had given us a lecture in the finer points of local stone for wall building, half the stone Peter had heaved painfully into the trailer was back in our garden.

"How's th'old cat I give 'ee then?"

"Brandy? He's fine, look," I pointed to where the cat stretched languorously on a warm patch of earth.

"Brandy you call him, what's that, for his colour? He has got a bit o' ginger in him I s'pose." Old Walt looked at the cat. I couldn't tell him that we had christened the cat Bran after Peter's prescribed treatment for his donor's stoppage. But the children had not liked the name and it had become Brandy.

"You want to get something planted in that bit of ground where th'old cat is."

I nodded, "it's the only clean bit of soil we could dig over until we've cleared this stone. I was going to put a few flowers in."

Walt snorted, "flowers, plenty of time for flowers when you've got more ground cleared. I'll bring 'ee some purple sproutin' plants. My old uncle used to live in this cottage and he had his privy pit about there. That must be a good bit of dirt, grow anything there you will. You get it dug over and I'll fetch 'ee the plants." He stumped away down the lane.

Peter began shifting stone again but this time on a one-for-the-trailer, one-for-the-wall-repair basis. Soon his bare torso was streaked with dirt and sweat. The afternoon was becoming very warm.

"You the doctor then?"

A young lad with a towel wrapped round his arm stared at us in disbelief from the gateway. Peter winced as he unbent his back. Then he saw the lad's arm and his face lit up. A casualty, something to relieve him from manual labour.

He jumped down from the wall. "Yes, come in. Been in the wars have you?

"I bin bit by a fox," the lad announced with pride.

Peter looked startled but led him through the kitchen door. I was left to continue the stone picking. Through the window I saw Peter unwrap the towel from the lad's arm. I thought of the sterile trolleys I would have laid up for Peter in the Casualty Department where we had worked. Our kitchen was not well equipped. Within minutes Peter was on the kitchen doorstep beckoning to me.

"This lad was told to come to me because the foxes round here have got distemper. How the hell do I treat distemper in humans?" he hissed.

We stared at each other. London casualty departments had taught us how to treat heroin addicts and meths drinkers but distemper was not common in the human population of London.

"How did you get this fox bite?" I asked the lad who was sitting on a kitchen chair with his arm resting on the table.

He looked embarrassed. "He got caught in one of my rabbit snares and he weren't too happy when I found him."

Peter thought fast. "I'll clean up the wound and dress it. Are you up to date on your tetanus jabs?" The lad turned pale.

"Come into surgery on Monday morning and we can check in your notes. We can give you a boost then if you need it." I guessed that Peter would do some quick telephoning before Monday to check up on distemper too.

When the lad had disappeared down the lane with a bandage round his arm I put the kettle on to make tea. Before the kettle boiled the telephone rang.

"I'll get it," I shouted to Peter who was washing his hands.

"Is that the doctor's house. Oh thank goodness," the woman's voice on the other end sounded agitated. "This is Mary Pringle speaking. You know my mother I think, she telephones sometimes when I go out."

"Yes indeed." I was speaking to 'I'm Dying's' daughter.

"Mother's hearing aid battery ran out at lunch time and she wouldn't take her tablets,"

I struggled to follow Mary Pringle's confused story.

"I've had such a battle with her," she went on. "I tried to get her to take the tablets with her cup of tea just now and she swallowed her hearing aid battery instead. These new ones are so tiny," She was on the edge of tears.

"I'll get my husband to speak to you, Miss Pringle."

I put the phone down and went into the kitchen, closing the door carefully behind me. "Guess what?" I giggled, " I'm dying has swallowed her hearing aid battery in mistake for her tablets."

I got a stern look from Peter. "It's not funny," he said heading for the phone, "those hearing aid batteries contain mercury. She really will be dying if I don't do something quick."

"Can we have something to drink? We're hot." The children appeared at the kitchen door. As I opened the fridge to take out milk for our tea and a bottle of fruit juice there was a commotion in the garden. Brandy shot through the kitchen with his fur on end. Milk bottle in hand I looked over the children's shoulders to see a group of boys, one with a snarling dog, walking up the side path. The dog was straining at the inadequate piece of baler twine threaded through his collar. I hauled the children into the kitchen as the group reached the back door.

"This dog just bit I," claimed the boy who was holding the dog. His supporters nodded and broke into a chorus of explanations. The accused mongrel bared his teeth as if looking for another victim. I took a step back. "Where did he bite you?"

"Up the Drang. He were running loose." said the boy giving the high-walled lane which ran behind the High Street its older name. Officialdom had put up a sign calling it Jubilee Lane.

"I meant where is your injury?" I was conscious of Peter's voice in the background organising an ambulance for Mrs Pringle. Our tea stood cooling on the table behind me.

"He got I in the bum," the injured lad said glumly, his companions confirming this with grins and nods.

"Well first of all, the rest of you lads can take this dog away before it bites someone else," I said in my best staff nurse's voice, "and you can come in and the doctor will look at your - er injury." One of the boys took hold of the length of baler twine and jerked the dog away from our back door. The rest trailed reluctantly after him.

"Hang on," I leaned out of the door and called after them, "I don't suppose the dog's got distemper has it?"

They stared at me. "How should we know, he 'ent our dog."

By the time Peter had sorted out Mrs Pringle and the boy's punctured bottom the tea was cold.

"I'll make a fresh pot," I said, carrying the cold tea out to toss it where Walt Ford said his uncle had buried the contents of his privy.

Peter looked at the kitchen table with distaste. "I don't think I want to drink tea here until you've disinfected the table staff nurse!"

The children had fallen asleep with the cat on the lawn so we took our tray of tea and tiptoed to the front garden. Peter pulled two grubby old deck chairs out of the shed and we sank into them. We had drunk our tea and were falling asleep in the sunshine, worn out by stone picking, when a genteel cough attracted our attention from the gate.

"Excuse me for disturbing your Saturday afternoon, doctor," the lady said in tones which belied her apology. "But I need a prescription before the chemist closes for the weekend."

Peter sat up blinking into the afternoon sun. The woman's grey hair was pulled into such a tight bun that the skin was strained at her temples giving her a wild-eyed look.

Peter frowned. "There was a surgery this morning."

"I am aware of that but I was not aware that I had run out of my Phenobarbitone. I must have a supply for the weekend."

I watched Peter for his reaction. Phenobarbitone was an old fashioned tranquillizer; barbiturates, so popular when we had trained, had gone out of fashion. I knew that Peter would be keen to wean Dr Thomas's patients off barbiturates. I wondered if he would tackle that job in the garden on a Saturday afternoon.

"I think the best thing is if you come into surgery on Monday morning and we have a chat about this, Mrs Er -" he said in his best friendly doctor voice.

"It's Miss Macdonald and I must have some for the weekend, Rover needs them."

"Rover?" Peter sat upright.

The woman moved into the gateway and I saw that she was holding a snarling dog – the one we had met earlier – on a lead.

"Is that your dog?" I asked in amazement. She looked more the type for a quiet spaniel.

"Yes. Rover is a darling dog as long as he has the tablets. But without them he can be rather naughty." Rover snarled. "He got out into the lane this afternoon and I have had a most disagreeable scene with some village boys who claim that he bit one of them."

Peter heaved himself out of his deck chair. "Do you mean that you feed your phenobarbitone to the dog?"

Miss Macdonald blushed and looked over her shoulder before lowering her voice. "You see, doctor, the pills were so wonderful when I had The Change that when Rover started biting people and being naughty I tried them on him and they work wonders."

I tried to imagine a menopausal Miss Macdonald snarling like Rover.

"I really cannot give you a prescription on the NHS for tranquillizers for your dog, Miss Macdonald," Peter said, "I'm sorry."

"In that case," she glared at us, "I shall remove my name from your list and join Dr Jones's practice in Moreton. Come on Rover."

We watched as she dragged the dog back up the lane towards the village. Peter groaned softly as he sat down again.

"My first weekend on duty and what happens? I start losing patients from my list and discover that I should have trained as a vet to practice medicine around here."

"Never mind," I said soothingly. "You probably saved Mrs 'I'm Dying' from dying, didn't you?"

Peter snorted. "Some poor surgeon is spending his afternoon fishing around in her insides for a hearing aid battery so that she can continue to make her daughter's life miserable."

"I expect her daughter would be even more miserable without her. People are like that."

"I suppose you're right," Peter sighed and looked at the pile of stone. He was saved by the bell as the telephone rang again. "I'll get it," he said jumping from his deck chair. I got up more warily. I was once tangled in a collapsed deck chair when I was nine months pregnant so I treat deck chairs with caution.

Peter reappeared buttoning his shirt. "Got to go to a farm accident. I've left the address on the phone pad."

"Any phone number?"

"They didn't have time to tell me," he said, sprinting towards the car.

"So how do I get hold of you if I get another urgent call?"

"You'll think of something," Peter threw himself in the car and started the engine. He put his head out of the window as he backed out into the lane. "If in doubt dial 999," he shouted.

I carried the tea tray back into the kitchen and put it on the draining board. I searched for disinfectant to swab the kitchen table, then remembered I had used it all up on the hall floor. "Hot soapy water will have to do," I muttered. I was scrubbing the table when the telephone rang again.

"My husband has just put the hedge trimmer across his hand," the voice on the other end sounded frantic, "there's blood everywhere."

"Put a tourniquet on and dial 999," I said quickly. "Dr Stratford has just gone out."

"Where?"

I glanced at the phone pad, "Ridgeway Farm."

"That's down the lane from us, I'll send my son."

The line went dead. Country people don't call ambulances readily, they still seemed to have great faith in their local GP.

Before I could turn away the telephone rang again.

"Mrs Stratford. Mary Pringle. I just thought doctor might like to know that the hospital found the battery in mother's stomach. They said it could have poisoned her. I don't know how to thank you and your husband. I would never have forgiven myself if I had poisoned my own mother!"

When I put the telephone down minutes later I reflected that many daughters might have been tempted to dispatch Mrs Pringle themselves. I also realised that if Mrs Pringle had made that call herself in her usual way, claiming that she was dying, I might have treated it like her regular calls and then had to answer for my neglect to the coroner. I stood on the back doorstep staring over the sunlit fields enamelled with buttercups. There was clearly more to this rural practice than we had ever imagined. I began to wonder what sort of life we had let ourselves in for.

Our social life began one chilly evening in early May. We had been invited to a supper party at a farm. I managed to get the children off to sleep and, dressed in a long skirt, I waited for Peter to finish surgery. When he rushed into the house it was already half past eight.

"Sorry, love. Sod's law, surgery went on forever and I still have one visit to do."

"Where is the baby-sitter?"

"Oh God!" he clutched his forehead, "I forgot all about Charmaine. Okay, okay I'll go and get her now."

He returned ten minutes later with a very sulky looking teenage girl who glared at me as she sat down on a kitchen chair to rub her shins. I explained where she could find things in the kitchen cupboards and how to pacify the children if they woke up. She remained more interested in her shins.

"Charmaine had a problem in the car," Peter explained.

"Yeah, well I 'ent used to sharing space in a Mini with a bloody Zimmer frame, an oxygen cylinder and I don't know what else." Charmaine rubbed her bruised shins aggressively.

"Oh dear, I am sorry, Charmaine. The chocolate biscuits are in here," I opened the biscuit tin in an effort to placate her.

"I don't have to answer the "phone do I?" She said suspiciously.

"No, no, we are not on duty," I looked at Peter, "at least, I didn't think we were."

"We're not. I've transferred the phone to Dr Thomas for the night. I just have to do this one last visit. It won't take long I promise. Nothing for you to worry about at all, Charmaine. Come on, Annie, let's go."

Peter only calls me Annie when he is trying to be really nice for some reason. I picked up my skirt and followed him out to the car where he wedged the Zimmer frame on the back seat and put the oxygen cylinder behind the passenger seat in deference to my shins. We hurtled in silence along the darkening lanes to do his late house call.

"You do know where we are don't you?" I peered out of the windscreen at an unfamiliar landscape.

"Trust me, Annie. Here we are," he cried triumphantly as he swung the car into a farm gateway.

"Won't be long." Peter leapt out of the car with his bag and vanished into a house visible to me only where the gables were outlined against the moon. I shivered. I had been too vain to put an old cardigan over my evening outfit. I reached back to see if there was a travel rug under the Zimmer frame. The car began to rock. Something was pushing the Mini. Nervously I wound a side window down a fraction. Cold air rushed in and with it noises, the noises that a lot of large animals make. Peter had parked the car beside a hay dispenser. I was between a herd of cows and their evening snack. The car continued to rock as heavy bodies pushed past. Then I heard a door open and voices in the dark.

"Goodnight then, Mr Brown. I'll call again tomorrow." In the wedge of light from an open door I saw Peter stop and look for the car which was submerged in a herd of cows. He advanced using his bag as a weapon. "Mind out you stupid animals." He pushed and fought his way over to the car. As he wrenched the door open the nearest cow lifted her tail and deposited a load of dung.

"Missed me, you silly moo," Peter cried with triumph as he flung himself into the car. He started the engine and reversed out of the yard. As the engine warmed the inside of the car I sniffed, "I don't think she did miss you know. You smell."

We reached the farm owned by our host for the evening exactly one hour late.

"Now what?" Peter moaned as the car headlights picked up a wire stranded across our way to the house. "Electric fence. We'll have to leave the car here, love."

I got out of the car gingerly. I couldn't see what was underfoot but I could smell it and I was wearing my best shoes.

"So how do we get over that?" I said when we stood by the wire.

"Limbo dance?"

"You might be able to but I'm not going to try to limbo dance in a yard awash with moo-poo." I hitched my long skirt up around my thighs. " I don't much fancy jumping either in these shoes. But failing to clear this fence could have painful consequences. It might have been easier in daylight but never mind."

"My fault, so I'll jump first, then I can catch you," Peter took a run at the fence and landed on his feet – just. I did the same. He hung on to me and for a moment we skated gracefully, like ice dancers, across the farmyard. Somehow we arrived on the doorstep of the farmhouse still upright, our shoes generously manured. Peter rang the doorbell. I prayed that inside the door would be a flagstoned floor. The door opened to reveal our smiling hostess. Behind her were acres of pale wall-to wall carpet.

"I'm so sorry - "I started but she cut me short."

"No problem, we were all quite happy waiting with our drinks. Come on in."

We wiped our shoes on the doormat and followed her into a large room where a group of people was gathered around a log fire with glasses in their hands. As the introductions were made Peter murmured our apologies with the magic words, 'an emergency call.' He received their understanding comments as his due.

By the time we went into the dining room I was extremely hungry. A beef casserole was brought to the table wafting a savoury smell of such intensity, past my nose, that I felt like a Bisto Kid. I was about to sink my fork into my portion of fragrant meat when a conversation between all the farmers at the table made me pause.

"How heavy was this one at slaughter then, John?" asked the young man on my left.

"Oh, about 600 Kilos."

I changed tactics and started on the buttery jacket potato also on my plate. The farmers went on to discuss the animal we were eating at length. I tried the carrots. By the time they had changed the subject I practically knew the animal's name and the colour of its eyes. I was also seriously tempted to convert to vegetarianism on the spot.

Over coffee and home-made Sloe Gin after the meal I listened to the young farmers' wives. They spoke of a world I did not know.

"Did you see Priscilla at the Hunt Ball last week?"

"Yes, she wasn't with Jeremy did you notice?"

"My dear, they haven't been seen together since they had that awful row at the Point-to-Point. Do tell me, what are you wearing to The Show this Year? We're on the Lord Lieutenant's table and I can't find a thing. What about you, Ann?" the elegant speaker turned to me, "are you and Peter going to The Show?"

I resisted the temptation to say 'what Show,' fearing a serious loss of rural Brownie Points and merely murmured that it would depend on Peter's off duty.

"My dear, of course, such a bore. Your life must be simply ruled by the telephone. You need a good old-fashioned house-keeper. You know, like the one in that TV series. What's it called – Dr Finlay's Casebook?" She put on a mock Scottish accent, "Arden Hoose, Dr Cameron's residence."

I smiled weakly at the hoots of laughter. Perhaps, I thought, these well dressed gels do sometimes have to remove mud from their floors but I doubted if they could even imagine orange lino tiles and puddles of diabetic pee.

At midnight the party broke up and we walked back towards our car with our fellow guests. Our host and hostess stood on their doorstep waving. In the light which streamed from the open door I could see our fellow guests' large cars. Our Mini was parked alone some distance away. I held my breath as we all approached the wire. One of the men nonchalantly held it aloft for the ladies. We walked underneath with no more than a dignified bow of the head.

"Funny isn't it," one of the women commented, "how just a bit of baler twine will keep cows out of a yard. Silly creatures."

I thought of calling the cows something stronger until I remembered that I had just eaten one of their friends.

"Goodnight."

"Hope we'll see you at The Show."

Their voices echoed as they got into their cars. The darkness hid our red faces. We were to learn that electric fences not only look different, they hum.

"What is this Show they were all talking about?" I asked Peter as he reversed the car out of the yard to follow the limousines gliding down the lane.

"The County Agricultural Show next month. I gather that I'm expected to help with the First Aid. We get free tickets if I do."

"It sounds like another of the Rights of Passage into rural life," I said. "Did you hear that conversation over dinner, the one about the beef?"

Peter chuckled. "I couldn't look at you."

"I shall invite them all back to dinner at our place," I promised rashly. "You can entertain them with accounts of gory operations and I shall serve them lentil soup and bean stew!"

"I wonder if such Upper Crust people suffer from wind," Peter said reflectively. "With a menu like that I think we might find out."

I giggled. "We've got another trial by knife and fork on Saturday at The Hall," I reminded him. "It is kind of all these people to invite us out but I think I'm beginning to suffer from culture shock."

The Hall was the sort of house that I would once have bought a ticket to enter. Peter and I were soon separated by the crowds in the elegant panelled rooms. I was beginning to enjoy myself until I heard raised voices. One of them was Peter's. I found him in the dining room where he had cornered his adversary. They stood, with plates of buffet food clutched to their chests, gesticulating at each other with their forks.

"How many weekends are you on call then?" Peter was demanding as I sidled up to his shoulder. " People think twice before they call you vets out. You can charge them for your nocturnal services."

"And how many different species do you treat?" The vet, who had a soft Irish accent, turned to me with a friendly wink. We had not been introduced but, as he told me later, only a wife would attempt to mediate in that sort of argument. "Your customers are all the same basic animal surely," he went on. "Now bulls and budgies are not, nor are cats and cows alike at all. The trouble is, since the Herriot books were published you all think our lives consist of delivering sweet woolly lambs and appealing calves."

"Rubbish," Peter took a stab at the salad on his plate. "James Herriot's working conditions were no picnic in the 1950's but surely you aren't telling me that your life is like that now." Peter ignored me and started on another line of argument. I decided that the vet could hold his own and I was not needed to mediate. I joined the queue of people moving slowly along a long table spread with buffet food.

"Never invite vets and doctors to the same party, they always argue," a red-faced man confided as we met over a dish of cole slaw. His plate was so heaped with rare beef that he couldn't make room for a lettuce leaf. I smiled at him, hoping he would not discover who I was and moved on to the next salad bowl. Out of the corner of my eye I saw our host parting Peter and the vet with a tray full of wine glasses.

"Come on, you two, drink to your differences," he bore Peter away to introduce him to someone else.

"Sorry about that," I said when I took my plate over to the deep windowsill where the vet had just balanced his glass of wine.

"Oh don't give it another thought," he treated me to another of his charming smiles, then said confidingly. "Actually I think your husband has taken on a hard task. The single-handed doctor is an endangered species. Like a lighthouse keeper his is a lonely and difficult job. But it wouldn't do to let him think that at this stage now would it? A little friendly sparring does wonders for a man's confidence and we are not exactly in competition are we? Mind you," he took a long drink of his wine. "Your husband's predecessor did once succumb to the temptation to offer one of my farmer clients a little free advice on the NHS."

"Oh dear," I remembered Miss Macdonald and Rover. "What for?"

"It was a cow with a spectacular rash. He correctly diagnosed that it was an allergy to a wild plant, and gave the farmer a bottle of gentian Violet from his dispensary to paint on the spots. I had a fine old time for weeks after that ribbing him about the NHS inflicting purple cows on the landscape."

Laughing, I asked, "how would you have treated the cow?"

"Oh probably the same way but I didn't tell him that! He would have had the hide off me if I'd treated one of his human patients with cow medicine." He reached over to pick up my empty glass, "let me go and refill this to fortify you. Initiation into rural life is very taxing."

As he went in search of the wine bottles I looked around the room and decided to enjoy the lighter side of life in the country.

# *Prescription for a New Surgery*

"I NEED A HAIR CUT," Peter announced one evening when we had been in the village for a few weeks. "I feel like a hippy."

I nodded, "if we were in Otterbury you could easily be mistaken for one." Otterbury was a town well known for its ancient abbey and its modern hippies.

"Mr Appleyard in Rock Cottage is the village barber," I said, displaying my new local knowledge. "His wife told me if you need a hair cut you just turn up at the cottage on a Friday evening."

Peter looked at James whose hair was also long. "What are we waiting for?"

It's the children's bedtime."

"Well, if barbers only work at bedtime around here then bedtime it will have to be. Come on you two." The children scrambled down from their places at the kitchen table. I started piling the dishes, then said, "oh blow this lot, it can wait. I want to see this village barber's shop too."

In single file we walked down the lane. Low evening light picked out the colours in the orchard blossom – every shade of pink from the lipstick-pink of the unopened buds to palest pink of the full blown cider-apple flowers. There were bluebells and cow parsley at the roadside.

"Isn't it beautiful?" I enthused.

"What?" Peter looked vaguely round.

"The apple blossom, all this," I swept my hand to take in the roadside verge.

"That is," Peter said as a sports car roared past us and we all flattened ourselves against the field wall. James jumped up and down with the same enthusiasm for speed. The lane went quiet when the car had roared away. A group of heifers, tearing at the long grass over the wall, raised their heads as Clare stopped to watch them in a gateway. The young animals clustered around the gate. Clare put her hand through but they backed away.

"Keep still and quiet, Clare, and they will come back," I told her, "cows are very curious."

Peter leaned his elbows on the gate. "One of my farmer patients told me that he was almost captured by the Germans in France during the war because of a few cows. Apparently he and a group of other soldiers were hiding from a passing German patrol behind a hedge when a group of cows came over to sniff at them and nearly gave their hiding place away."

The heifers came close enough for us to smell their hay- sweet breath as they sniffed at us through the gate bars.

"They've got wet noses," Clare giggled, " but I like their eyes." So did I. The heifers had the wide-eyed look of all young animals.

We reached Rock Cottage just as a man came out of the gate. "You're lucky, doctor, he said, "there's no queue."

"Er, where do we go?"

"In there," the man pointed to the garage at the side of the cottage. The doors of the garage stood open so we trooped in.

"Good evening, doctor, hair cut is it? Mrs Stratford, do sit down." Mr Appleyard, who had a face to match his name, dusted an old kitchen chair in the corner for me with his handkerchief. I sat down with James at my side and Clare on my knee. Peter sat in the barber's chair which stood in the centre of the garage. Mr Appleyard flung an old sheet around Peter and began to cut his hair.

"Mummy, what does he use those for?" James whispered as he looked at the garden shears and rakes which hung around the garage walls.

"Gardening love. This is Mr Appleyard's garden shed as well as his barber's shop."

James continued to look nervously around at the pots of paint and weedkiller in old bottles bearing the skull and cross bones with the word POISON in large print. The garage soon looked like Delilah's parlour as Peter's hair fell. Mr Appleyard's wife had told me that her husband had been an army barber. I could see that Peter was getting the shortest of short back and sides. When he had finished Mr Appleyard swept the sheet from Peter's shoulders and advanced on James, clippers in hand. Terrified by his strange surroundings, and the new view of his father's scalp, James shot out into Mr Appleyard's garden. Clare leapt off my lap and followed him.

"Another time perhaps," Mr Appleyard said comfortingly. "Can I offer you both a drop of my dandelion wine?"

"Why not," Peter whispered as we followed him out of the garage, "it might warm my head."

The garden overlooked a field where dandelion seedheads stood like grey-haired geriatrics among the newly enamelled buttercups.

"This is last year's of course," Mr Appleyard said as he handed us glasses of yellow wine. "I made this year's supply a few weeks ago."

I remembered pulling back the bedroom curtains one morning to see our field yellow with dandelions. The time had past so quickly that I had hardly noticed their ageing. I took a swig of the wine. My eyes watered. The home-made wine was as fierce as the colour of the setting sun. Mr Appleyard went to get some lemonade for the children. I caught Peter's eye. We both watered the nearest current bushes with the contents of our glasses. The dew was falling gently on the dandelion heads as we filed back along the lane. Peter occasionally rubbed his neck where he was clearly feeling the draught. We were all yawning.

"Early to bed I think," Peter eyed me with a speculative look.

"We're on duty from ten o'clock remember."

"Damn."

Every doctor knows that sex when on call is not a good idea. A telephone bell ringing loudly by your ear at the wrong moment is very traumatic. Other people had problems with the mating game that night too.

We went to bed early and had just fallen into a deep sleep when the telephone rang.

"Is that the doctor?" I heard a hoarse voice ask as Peter pulled the receiver down to his pillow.

"Yes," he answered sleepily.

The voice was female, young and embarrassed. "Doctor, you don't know me, I'm on holiday. We're camping at Church Farm. The thing is, I've run out."

"Run out of what?" Peter said patiently.

"You know, my pills."

Peter half sat up and reached for the pad beside the bed. "What are the tablets for?"

"You know," the caller struggled for words. "They're for you-know-what. THE pill!"

"Come to the surgery in the morning and I'll give you a prescription." Peter's hand was halfway towards putting the receiver back when there were noises in the background.

"Are you still there, doctor? Well can we or can't we? He wants to know."

"Ask him if he's a betting man," Peter said through gritted teeth. "I'll see you in surgery in the morning."

We had been asleep for about half an hour when the telephone rang again.

"Doctor, it's me, Tracey Jones," the voice giggled. "I'm ever so sorry to bother you but you see I'm 'phoning from Torquay. We're on holiday me and Aaron. I forgot to bring me pills."

"Go to the nearest surgery in the morning," Peter said, wearily lifting himself on one elbow to replace the 'phone. "Oh, and Tracey," he added, "it's all right for tonight." I could hear Tracey's giggles as he put the telephone down. Peter flopped on his pillow with a groan. "You'd think our Tracey would have had the decency to wake some Torquay GP. Why do I have to get the visitors *and* our holidaying patient's problems?"

❧

"It must be something to do with spring," Peter said the next day when he returned from morning surgery.

"Mind the kitchen floor – it's wet," I growled at him. "I've just washed it. What must be spring?"

"All this sex." Peter picked his way over the dry bits of floor to the fridge. "I've had patients panicking over broken condoms and three in this morning with what is euphemistically called honeymoon cystitis."

"Why call it euphemistic?" I snapped, "it's a very painful condition."

"I know," Peter stood up with a yogurt from the fridge in his hand, "it's the honeymoon bit that is the euphemism. Not one of this morning's girls was over fifteen. Sixteen is still the legal age for honeymoons isn't it. Anyway, why are you so grumpy?"

"I've just spent hours trying to get your spilled medicines off this floor." I looked with distaste at the lurid lino tiles.

"When it gets sticky underfoot I have to do something."

"Pity you didn't wait," Peter said cheerfully, "I've run out of indigestion mixture. I've got to make some more before this evening's surgery."

"Can't you make it at the surgery?"

"You know I can't, there isn't room." Peter was practising in the tiny annexe Dr Thomas had built on to the side of his house which was now for sale. We had tried every way we could think of to raise money to buy the old house, but without luck.

"I heard this morning that a developer wants to buy Dr Thomas's house,

Anne," Peter said when he had licked the last of the yogurt from his spoon.

I stared at him. "What will happen to your surgery?"

"I'm told it will be bulldozed. We've got to look for somewhere else – fast." As he spoke Peter went to the sink to add water to powdered indigestion mixture in a large Winchester bottle.

He was so phlegmatic about the possibility of being without a surgery that I hadn't the heart to be cross when he shook the bottle so vigorously that the loose cap flew off showering his trousers and my clean floor with chalky peppermint mixture.

"Sorry," he said when he came back downstairs in clean trousers, carrying his dirty ones.

"I wish we could afford a washing machine," I dunked the trousers in a bowl to soak. "Yesterday you got somebody's blood all over your shirt cuffs and last week you got plaster of Paris on your trousers when you were setting somebody's broken foot. Plaster has the consistency of old-fashioned wedding cake icing." But I was talking to myself. Peter had gone. Like all men he hates being nagged.

That evening he was very late home from surgery. When he did come in I was ironing.

"Annie," his voice made me turn round.

"Where on earth have you been?" I looked at his torn trousers and his filthy shirt. He carried his jacket by its collar. I could see that one of the arms was almost ripped off at the shoulder.

"Under a lorry." He sat on a kitchen chair and rolled up a trouser leg. His right knee was bruised and bleeding. I turned the iron off and got a bowl of water without asking more.

"The Fire Brigade had to use their winch to pull the crashed car out from under the lorry. Ouch!" he flinched as I cleaned the grit out of his knee. "I didn't see the winch wire."

"You fell over it, oh poor you."

"Poor me nothing. You should have seen the driver of the car."

"Any good?" I asked briefly. He shook his head and I could see from his expression that he had tried hard to save the driver.

"Pity you weren't wearing your armour-plated tweed suit," I said and raised the ghost of a smile from him. He nodded and looked at his old jacket. "There's oil as well as blood on this, it's not worth trying to mend the sleeve either. It's done for." Peter had worn the jacket as a medical student. Suddenly those distant days seemed very carefree and far away.

"On your next day off we'll go and buy you a new jacket," I said as I stood up to get some more clean water.

He nodded, "we'll go and buy a washing machine as well. To hell with the price – we need one. You managed all the nappies without one, I'm not having you hand-washing clothes like this." He looked down at his blood-stained trousers. "Poor devil," he muttered as he stood up and went wearily upstairs to have a bath.

The next morning Peter was subdued at breakfast. The children tried to liven him up by having a toast crust throwing competition which did nothing for his temper or mine. The children were suddenly silenced by the clatter of the cat flap as Brandy erupted into the kitchen carrying something in his mouth.

"Mummy, he's caught something!" James yelled as he leapt down from his chair and began to chase the cat around the kitchen.

"Sit down and keep still, James," Peter ordered as he began to stalk the cat. Brandy jumped on to the kitchen work-top. As Peter grabbed him Brandy opened his mouth to protest and dropped the bird which flew to the top of a kitchen cupboard. Stunned, we stared up. The indignant bird shook himself and stared back.

"Good grief, it's a Little Owl!" Peter caught Brandy by the scruff of his neck and put him out into the hall.

I looked up at the tiny owl blinking at us from on top of the cupboard. "How on earth did the cat get a Little Owl through the cat flap and how did he catch it?"

Peter latched the door into the hall firmly against Brandy.

"Perhaps the cat pounced when the owl had just caught something. Getting the bird through the cat flap wouldn't be difficult, it's more feathers than bird."

"Can we keep it," James breathed. Clare simply stared in wonder, her breakfast forgotten. The owl shook its ruffled feathers and stared back at us out of bright yellow eyes.

"Come on you lot out into the garden," Peter whispered, "if we leave the door open the owl should fly out."

It was no hardship to be in the garden on such a morning. A line of swallows perched like notes of music on the telegraph wires in the lane, and from our neighbour's bean row came a warm perfume.

G.Younger

"The broad bean flowers smell just like lily of the valley," I whispered.

"Give me broad beans on the plate any day," Peter said looking at his watch. "I must go in a minute or I'll have a waiting room full when I get to surgery."

"There he goes," James shouted as the Little Owl flew out of the kitchen door. We rushed to the garden wall. The bird perched for a moment to recover his composure on a field gatepost, then flew a low undulating path across the field.

"Right, I'm off." Peter unlocked the car, "I may be late for lunch – I've got a meeting with the developers who want to bulldoze the surgery."

"At least Brandy managed to cheer you up," I said to Peter. "Good luck with the developers."

When Joan put the telephone through to me that morning after surgery the calls were incessant. I was learning that my pharmaceutical knowledge was inadequate for my new job and my local knowledge non-existent. The first call that afternoon was typical.

"No, I'm sorry, the doctor isn't in at the moment. Can I help?" I said when I picked up the receiver with hands covered in garden soil. I was planting Walt Ford's promised purple sprouting plants.

"Her needs they pills - mutter mutter -"

"Sorry did you say the white pills?" I strained to hear the voice. " Oh sorry, I see. The right pills." I stopped writing, "right for what?"

"Her knees of course. You know she has they tablets what them body builders take."

Bewildered I asked, "Whose are the knees?

Granny's o' course. Granny Watkins. Been having them for years she has. En't done much for her body but they keeps her knees going."

"And the address?" I tried to sound efficient as I stood with my pencil poised. "Rose Cottage? Right, there will be a prescription at the surgery for you to collect this afternoon.

By the time Peter finally returned for his lunch I had a list of visits for him to do and prescriptions to write.

"What's this one?" Peter glared at my writing. "Watkins, Rose Cottage? Half the population of this village is called Watkins and I've seen at least three Rose Cottages already." He inspected his salad.

"It's a Granny Watkins and it sounds as if Dr Thomas had her on steroids for a knee problem."

Peter snorted, "he seems to have had every patient on steroids. I suppose they were the latest thing for arthritis in the 1950's and he saw no reason to change to anything better. It's a wonder the village isn't full of grannys with bulging biceps." He turned his lettuce over.

"Is there something wrong with your lunch ?"

Peter put his knife and fork down. "I went to get a blood sample from George Warren this morning. Joan told me that he never turns up at the surgery and as he's on Warfarin he needs his regular blood test."

I nodded. Warfarin, known to local people as rat poison, is an effective thinner of blood to prevent heart attacks. Regular tests are done to ensure that the blood doesn't become so thin that the patient bleeds easily.

"I caught him in his garden digging," Peter continued. "He said it was a fair cop and quite happily pulled his sleeve up and rested his forearm on his spade handle."

"Not the easiest of positions for hitting a vein first time," I sympathised.

"That wasn't the problem," Peter cut into his tomato. "I scored a bulls-eye. My syringe was just filling nicely when a hairy green caterpillar came trundling down his arm. For one mad moment I thought it was after his blood."

Peter picked an imaginary speck of grit off his lettuce with the tip of his knife. "Now, let's sort out these calls and the prescriptions I'm supposed to write. What's this?" he stabbed my list with his knife, "water tablets for scribble scribble, how do you expect me to know whose they are?" His tone reminded me of the ward sister to whom I once presented a whole row of unmarked specimen jars full of urine for testing. Resisting the temptation to make comments on his illegible handwriting I diverted his attention by asking about his meeting with the developers.

He sat back, "it's quite simple, they've bought the property and they intend to demolish the old house to build a block of flats."

"But it's such a nice old house," I protested. "So what happens to the surgery?"

Peter ran his fingers through the half inch of hair Mr Appleyard had left him. "I think I've persuaded them to let me buy a piece of land close to the road and the bus stop. We'll have to build a surgery."

"But we haven't got any money."

"Then we'll have to find some," Peter said grimly. "And before that I'll have to find somewhere to practice while we build. The bulldozers move in next month."

At half past four, when Joan took over the telephone, I took the children for a walk. We went along a lane we had not explored before. We passed a newly built bungalow where an old lady pottered in her garden. James whispered, "Mummy, she's got her slippers on."

Hearing voices the old lady turned towards us. Her face, like crumpled brown paper, split into a wide smile.

"Hello my darlin's," she came over to her wall. "Want to come in and see my hens then?" She gave me a friendly glance but her attention was concentrated on the children. She opened the gate and they followed her. "Mrs Lee's my name."

"You've got a nice new bungalow here, Mrs Lee," I commented as she led us past its stark concrete block walls.

"Bungalow?" She spat on the path and the children's eyes lit up. "What do I want with a bungalow? Me grandson Sam built it. Oh he's a good lad and he means well but I don't want no bungalow. That's where I live." Proudly she stood back to let us look into the paddock at the rear of the bungalow where a long caravan stood.

"That's my mobile home that is. I've had 'ee since I come off the road. I was brought up in a van, a proper one," she gave me a quick look, "a gypsy caravan, my grandmother's. They burned the van when she died, proper like, so I got this one and settled down." She coughed fruitily. "The damp do strike up through me slippers and give I this hoasty throat. I told my grandson nobody ever died of a hoasty throat but he would have it that I had to have a bungalow." Her smile returned, "you come and see my hens."

The children raced through the long grass of the paddock. "I bought 'em from a battery," Mrs Lee explained to me as we walked more slowly towards the hen run. "I could o' cried when I seen 'em, no feathers on, some blind, some missin' lumps of flesh. I told the man what brought 'em, 'I can't put they out in me garden. I'd get reported.' That's why I put 'em round the back here. Poor little beggars. Look all right now though don't they?"

The hens looked perfectly content, scratching about in their run, a patch of paddock which they had turned into their own dusty desert.

"You got lettuces in your garden?" Mrs Lee asked as we walked on past her vegetable patch. "I can't bend to plant no more but Jim, the postman, he puts a few bits in for me and I d'give he Marsy bars, that's what he likes, Marsy bars. I got too many lettuces though, I can't eat all they." She poked one with the toe of her slipper, "he's hearted up nice, you take he home later.

Come and see inside my caravan."

I called the children and we followed Mrs Lee. Inside her caravan Mrs Lee showed the children her treasures, shelves of polished brass and cut glass ornaments. Then she sighed. "It wont look the same over there," she glared out of the window at the bungalow.

"Mrs Lee," an idea was forming slowly in my mind. "What are you going to do with the van after you've moved into the bungalow."

"Sam says he's taking it for scrap. Says it's no good to nobody."

"I can think of somebody who would be very glad of it, for a short time anyway." Briefly I explained that the builders would soon be demolishing the old surgery. "We've managed to buy a bit of the land and if we can raise the cash we will have a new surgery built. But my husband needs somewhere to practice until it's finished."

Mrs Lee sat down heavily on the long cushioned seat under the end window of the big living van, "you reckon the doctor could use my old van? I'd like that. I'd be real proud. I don't bother doctors much myself but I'd like to think that folks would go to my old van for healing."

"I would have to ask him of course," I said hastily, seeing the pleasure on her face and trying to picture Peter's expression when he set eyes on the old caravan.

"There's no lav mind," Mrs Lee told me, "I go out the back, "but there's a sink look," proudly she showed me an enamel sink and draining board. "You bring the doctor along to see it when you can. I'll ask me grandson about shiftin". He's been on at me now for months to get me things over there but I haven't wanted to." Her eyes were twinkling. "I reckon I could settle happier in that concrete place knowing the old van was being put to good use."

"It wouldn't be for long, Mrs Lee," I warned her, "as soon as the new surgery was ready the van would have to be moved to make way for cars to be parked I expect."

"That's all right my dear," she patted my hand with her wrinkled brown one. "We all got to go sometime. But we want to be useful at the end don't we? Not left to rot. I'll ask me grandson if he could get a lorry and trail the van to the village. Just fancy, my old van, the doctor's surgery!"

❧

"You've got a what!" Peter came home from surgery tired and irritable. If I thought my wonderful idea was going to cheer him up I was wrong. "I can't do surgery in an old gypsy caravan."

"It isn't the sort of van you're thinking of. It's not one of those gypsy waggons you see in pictures, I'm not completely stupid," I said indignantly. "It's a mobile home. There's space for a waiting room and Mrs Lee's bedroom would make a small consulting room for you. And there's another little bedroom which you could use as an examination room."

"And the dispensary?" Peter was beginning to look half interested. He had spent all day trying to find suitable rooms to rent in the village without success.

"The kitchen would make a small dispensary. It"s not exactly the latest in designer health centres but it is on offer. Have you had any better ideas?"

Peter slumped into a chair. "No I haven't. There are the branch surgeries but neither of them is really suitable for full time use."

On Tuesdays Peter did a surgery in the Red Cross Hut in a nearby village; the Friday branch surgery took place in the lounge bar of a pub in another village.

"The Red Cross hut is used by the playgroup every morning and the pub rooms are only free after hours." Peter ran his fingers through his hair, "I suppose that leaves your caravan."

"We will own the land soon won't we?" I said eagerly. "If you work in the caravan parked on the site you can keep an eye on the builders.

"I suppose so." Peter's voice was tinged with doubt and the beginning of hope.

A month later Mrs Lee's mobile home, emptied of all her possessions, made stately progress through the village, pulled by an ancient lorry. The small patch of land, which we had bought with money borrowed from Peter's parents, was ready. Beyond our new fence the builders were busy tearing up the garden of Doctor Thomas's house. The old surgery stood waiting for the bulldozer. Our patch of land was at the roadside close to the village bus stop. It had been a wild corner of the doctor's garden. Now, in late May, it was full of white lilac, lacy drifts of cow parsley and granny's bonnets, pink flowers with petals arranged in triple-goffered layers, so justifying the country name for this flower. I picked a bunch for the cottage and promised myself that I would return when the flowers were over to collect seeds for the cottage garden.

Where the trees in the old garden had been felled, the site for the new surgery was marked out with stakes in the ground. A small patch of mown grass awaited the caravan. Peter and I stood at the side of the road to watch as Mrs Lee's grandson began the difficult manoeuvre of backing the long mobile home into place. Mrs Lee sat in comfort in our car with the children. She looked as excited as they did. By the time the long caravan was being positioned a sizeable audience of villagers had gathered to watch. When the van finally settled into place Mrs Lee got herself out of the car with the children and we all went over to congratulate her grandson on his driving skill.

"Well done, Sam," Peter rushed up to the lorry as Sam jumped down. "How much do I owe you for that fancy bit of driving?"

"A tenner?" Sam looked around speculatively. "And first pick of that wood?" He pointed to the felled trees piled at the edge of the site. "Or did you have somebody in mind for the wood?"

Peter looked vague, "no, not at all. We were wondering how to get it cleared. I want some good logs for the cottage fire for next winter but there's much too much here for us."

"I'll have me first month's rent in kind then," Mrs Lee said coming up behind her grandson. "You can make me a nice log pile by that concrete hen house you've built for me Sam."

Sam grinned. "I'll start logging up tomorrow if that's all right with you, doctor?"

"Fine," Peter said and I could see that his attention was not on the wood. He wanted to get inside the caravan and start trying to turn it into a temporary surgery.

## *Bodies and Babies*

I WOULDN'T WORRY ABOUT NOT having no lav' here, doctor," Mr Finch the sexton said to Peter the day before we opened the caravan as a temporary surgery. "Churches don't have no facilities neither. You know what they always say don't you?" Peter looked mystified. Mr Finch winked at me, "the grass is always greener outside the vestry door."

We were painting the partitions which Mr Finch, who doubled as sexton and village carpenter, had put up for us in the caravan. With his help we now had two hatches. One enabled Joan to direct the patients who came up the caravan steps into the 'waiting room.' Through the other she could pass patients' notes to Peter.

I don't know what the patients are going to make of this," Peter said as he set his medicines out on the kitchen shelves which had so recently held Mrs Lee's pots and pans.

"If they know what's good for them they'll just be grateful that we've got a surgery," Mr Finch said soothingly as he nailed up the sign which said Waiting Room over the entrance to Mrs Lee's living room. "Plenty of villages have lost their surgery along with their shops and their post offices. We're lucky. Mind you, doctor, I expect you'll find some who'll complain. Especially the fat ones who have to get undressed in here." He moved to nail the sign which read, 'Examination Room' over the slip of a room in which a fold-up bed was to do duty as an examination couch.

"Don't you worry, doctor," he tapped the nails in gently. "I'm putting these signs up so's they'll come down easy. You'll be putting them up again on the doors of your smart new surgery in no time. You'll be able to watch them new walls going up from here." He peered through the small windows of the caravan to where the builders were already busy digging the foundations of the new surgery.

Peter stood in the doorway and looked at the folding bed. "It's not the walls going up that I'm worried about just now, Mr Finch. I'm more worried about that bed going up, or even down, at the wrong moment. It's not very stable."

Mr Finch grinned. "Yes it could be nasty if 'e decided to fold up under somebody just when you had your finger - umm, leave it with me, doctor, I'll fix it so's that bed will stay still for you."

On the other side of the partition I smiled to myself as I slapped paint on to the bare wood. "What would we do without you, Mr Finch?"

He popped his head round the door, "what would we all do without you and the doctor, that's what I say. We'll soon have this place ready for customers on Monday."

"We won't have your help after today presumably," I said wiping up paint splashes from the lino floor. "You'll be on duty in church tomorrow."

"I'll be up Eastcombe tomorrow," he said, naming the collection of farms and houses a mile away which would have been called a hamlet but for the tiny church which qualified Eastcombe as a village.

"Something special on?"

"Rogation Sunday, we got the Rural Dean coming. You been up to see Eastcombe church yet have you?"

I shook my head, "I keep meaning to but we get so few Sundays off."

"We're off this Sunday, Anne if you want to go," Peter said from his "consulting room" where we had squeezed a very small desk and two chairs in place of Mrs Lee's bed and clothes rail.

"But there's all this to do," I gestured with my paint brush, adding more splashes to the floor.

"We'll have to finish the painting by tonight in time to let it dry," he reminded me, "in the morning I've got Joan and two district nurses coming to help me to empty the boxes of patient's notes and file them on Mr Finch's shelves. You go and hear the Rural Dean if you want to. You could take the children with you, we can't expect Mrs Hayward to have them again tomorrow."

We were managing to get a lot done in a short time because Mrs Hayward had offered to have James and Clare for the day. "You take them off for an hour or so, then bring sandwiches for the helpers up here."

On Sunday morning I scrubbed paint off my hands and dressed the children in their best clothes.

"I don't want to go to church," James said in ominous tones as I drove up the steep road towards Eastcombe. "I want to help Daddy."

"We're going to take him a picnic later," I explained. The road turned a sharp corner and I had to brake hard; a parked car almost blocked the narrow lane.

"Thoughtless road hog," I muttered, staring at the gateway in which the car could so easily have been pulled off the road. As I drove slowly past I saw the back of a figure in the gateway in the unmistakable pose of a man peeing. The only unusual feature was that this man was busy keeping his cassock up.

"What is that man in the black dress doing?" James said as I put my foot on the accelerator and shot up the hill.

"Contemplating nature," I said with some regard for the truth.

When we arrived in Eastcombe I parked where the rest of the congregation parked, in the farmyard. The church was reached through a wicket gate in the yard.

"This is a funny church," James looked disapprovingly at the cow pats on the path.

"I like it," Clare whispered. We went in through a door so low that I ducked, and I am not tall. Inside I saw Mr Finch pulling vigorously on a bell-rope.

I ushered the children into a pew at the back of the tiny church which was almost full. When Mr Finch stopped pulling on the bell rope a familiar robed figure stepped out from behind a curtained corner. Eastcombe church was so small that it didn't have a vestry. So the Rural Dean could not have popped out of a vestry door to water the grass outside even if he had waited.

"That's the man we saw … " James began.

"Shut up," I hissed in a fierce whisper.

"You said we weren't ever allowed to say that," James said in injured tones. "You said we had to say 'be quiet' because shut up is rude and I saw him … " luckily the organist chose that moment to start the harmonium wheezing. The children knelt facing backwards in the pew to watch as the organist produced music, of a sort, out of his ancient instrument.

When the Rural Dean gathered his cassock skirts up to mount the steps of the tiny pulpit I wondered if he had seen us in the car that sped away earlier. Even a stout, phlegmatic looking clergyman might be disconcerted to look down from the pulpit into the eyes of a female who had just seen him watering the hedge. I bit my lip to keep myself from smiling as he took his text from the reading for Rogation day; in sonorous tones he declared,

"For the Lord your God is bringing you to a rich land, a land of streams, of springs and underground waters gushing out in hill and valley ... " I could not look up at the Rural Dean in case I caught his eye.

I concentrated my attention on the only stained glass window in the plain Norman church. The scene in the window was a sentimental Victorian depiction of the nativity but the artist had used a local background. Behind the figures of the kings and shepherds, were cottages, green fields and a willow lined brook. To entertain the children I pointed out the pictures in the window and kept them quiet until I heard the Rural Dean closing his sermon with the words, 'bless the Lord your God for the rich land that he has given you.' I had a vague notion that he had been speaking about the poor in Africa when I was not paying attention. Guiltily I put more money in the collection than I intended. After the service I met up with Mr Finch in the churchyard where people stood chatting in the sunshine.

"What do you think of Eastcombe then?"

"It's very pretty," I said, looking round at the cluster of house roofs and barn gables beyond the raised churchyard.

"Terrible place to dig graves this is," Mr Finch said kicking at the grass. "Last grave I dug here was for a retired Archdeacon. When they tried to lower the coffin the hole weren't big enough. Mind 'ee were a big chap that Archdeacon. See that corner down there, " he pointed, " I dug a grave there once and he filled up with rain water. When they come to plant the coffin they found it wouldn't stay down, 'ee were floating! Graves do take some digging in this stony soil. You tell the doctor from me to keep his patients alive. I don't want to do no digging this week, I've got the screws."

"Not from all the work you've done in the caravan I hope?" I said with half an eye on the children who were playing hide-and-seek around the table-tombs.

"No, a bit of woodwork never hurt I, it's the digging that gives I the screws."

Unfortunately Peter was not able to keep all his patients alive in the busy weeks that followed. Surgeries took much longer in the caravan and I had some unusual home calls, the first when Peter was at the Cottage Hospital seeing his patients one afternoon. James was upstairs in bed suffering from tonsillitis, Clare was having an afternoon sleep and I was trying to catch up on some of the surgery typing which Joan had been unable to complete in the caravan. I was doing a three finger job on our old typewriter at the kitchen table when the front doorbell rang.

"Damn," I got up reluctantly and went to the door.

"Is the doctor at home?" the tall man on the doorstep was oddly dressed for a warm summer afternoon in a dark suit and black tie.

"No I'm afraid he's at the hospital. Can I help?"

"I doubt it," I glanced over his shoulder and was startled to see a hearse parked outside the cottage.

"We've just picked up a lady who collapsed in the village." The man told me in lugubrious tones." No one seems to know her so I thought if I brought her here the doctor might know who she is."

"You mean you've got a corpse out there?" As I spoke I was relieved to see Peter driving down the lane. The undertaker went down the path to explain his problem to Peter. I went out to stand by the wall nervously glancing up and down the lane hoping that no one would chose that moment to walk their dog past the cottage. The undertaker opened the back of the hearse, pulled out the trolley and uncovered the draped figure.

"We can see the lady," voices above me carolled and I looked up to see to children leaning out of their bedroom window.

The next problem arrived one evening a week later when the children were safely asleep. Peter was dozing in a chair, worn out after a week of frequent night calls. I was reading quietly when a car drew up outside.

"I'll go," I said as I got up to answer the door.

"I'm so sorry to trouble you," a stout lady stood in the light from our hallway. "I've come from the dog training class," I glanced past her and saw that her car appeared to be full of barking dogs. I was about to tell her that she was not at the vet's house when she went on, "it's my friend, I always give her a lift home with her dogs. She doesn't feel very well so I thought the best thing was to come straight here."

Peter came out of the room behind me, blinking in the light.

"Can you bring her in?" he asked but she shook her head.

"She can't seem to move, doctor, can you come and look?"

I went out to the car with Peter in case I could help. But neither of us could help the lady who was wedged in the back seat of a very small car full of dogs. She was dead.

Her friend was surprisingly philosophical, "Can't think of a nicer way to go," she said later over the cup of tea I had made while we waited for the undertaker and the coroner's officer to arrive. "She loved her dogs."

The three noisy dogs, shut in our garage, were still barking.

"She often told me she didn't want to get too old to look after her dogs. She wanted to go to bed one night and not wake up. I should think she'd be tickled pink at the idea of popping off like that in the car with the dogs." The stout lady took another biscuit and I was impressed again by the resilience of human beings.

I didn't see Mrs Lee, during the time when she was settling into her new home, until she arrived on my doorstep out of breath one summer afternoon. "Can you send the doctor up me daughter's caravan quick,"

"What's the problem Mrs Lee?" I stabbed the last peg into a line of washing.

"Her baby's comin'." Mrs Lee flopped down on the old bench outside the kitchen door to catch her breath.

"Don't worry," I picked up the wash basket and went in towards the telephone, "babies take their time."

Mrs Lee looked at me from under her bushy white eyebrows, "not when the mother's had eight already they don't and my Mavis has had them all quick."

I telephoned the Cottage Hospital.

"Is Dr Stratford still there, Sister? It's his wife, I've got an imminent delivery for him. Can you rustle up a district midwife too? Ask them to go to the caravan at Thornditch. Peter knows where that is. Tell him that Mavis is in labour with her ninth child." The sensible sister did not waste time on comment but promised to get help fast.

"Come on, Mrs Lee," I grabbed the keys of the second car we had just bought. It was only an old banger but it was already proving a lifeline for me. I could never borrow Peter's car and the village bus service simply did not enable me to get into the town and back between surgeries. James was at school and Clare at playgroup that morning.

"Who's with Mavis?" I asked as I drove at speed along the lanes.

"Her man." Mrs Lee said briefly, hanging on to her seat. She was not used to cars.

Thornditch was one of those corners of land so useful to travellers. It was a small quarry, long disused and overgrown with trees. With its back to the north the low rock face provided shelter in winter and privacy in summer. We arrived at almost the same time as Peter who jumped from his car with Nurse Jackson; they vanished inside the caravan. Mrs Lee went to talk to Mavis's man when he came down the caravan steps. Mrs Lee's grandchild was not being born in a traditional caravan but a decrepid old bus. From the design I guessed the bus had last been on the road in the 1950's. Tattered lace curtains hung at each window. To pass the time I got out of the car and looked at the wild flowers growing nearby. The edge of the old quarry was a natural rock garden with curtains of toadflax like tiny lavender snapdragons and splashes of stonecrop yellow against the grey stone. Tucked into crevices I found shining cranesbill, herb robert, rue-leaved saxifrage and valerian. I wondered if Mavis ever used them. Valerian is a good cure for sleeplessness and yarrow will help ease a cough; Mrs Lee was knowledgeable about herbs. Peter was impressed by the effect of the black mint which she grew. Chopped leaves steeped in hot water with a little honey make a delicious cure for indigestion or wind. We were already growing roots she had given us in the cottage garden.

I was just climbing towards what I thought was a rare rock rose when I heard a shout. Peter stood on the step of the old bus calling to Mrs Lee and Mavis's man. I scrambled down to hear the news.

"A little girl," Peter said as he rolled his shirt sleeves down. I glanced at the father and grandmother, they were both smiling.

"Last three was lads," Mrs Lee said to her son-in-law, "time you had a girl again. What you going to call her?"

The big man looked blank. Peter said, "Mavis has just asked me for ideas on that score too."

"What about, Rosie," I blurted out, my mind still full of the quarry flowers.

"Rosie," Mrs Lee experimented with the name. She looked at her son-in-law, How about that then?

Mavis's man thought for a minute and then said slowly, "well seeing as we're Smiths, not Lees, Rosie would be alright if our Mavis likes that. Rosie Lee wouldn't have done would it? She'd have got called cup-of-tea at school."

Mrs Lee lost patience with her son-in-law's slow thinking process, "I'll go and ask Mavis. Can I go in to her now, doctor?"

Peter stood aside on the old bus step. "Come aboard, Mrs Lee, come and see your latest grand-daughter. The midwife is just washing her." From inside the bus I heard the indignant cry of a strong newborn baby. I tried to imagine the quarry in winter; Rosie was going to have a hard childhood.

I left Mrs Lee with her family and drove back to the village to collect Clare from playgroup. As I walked with her from the hall where the playgroup was held a voice called me over to a cottage where Mr Robbins leaned on his gate.

"Got a letter for me have you, Mr Robbins?" I often took letters to the post office at the far end of the village for Mr Robbins who walked with two sticks.

"Not today." He gave me a toothless grin and produced something from behind his back. He presented me with a creamy rose, surrounded by a hoop of honeysuckle bound to the stem of the rose with raffia.

"Us calls he a Honeysuckle Rose," he said, "As lads us used to make them for our favourite girls."

"It is beautiful, Mr Robbins," I said and meant it. No florist's bouquet had ever looked so perfect or so artless.

"The rose is old," he said to cover his confusion, "I calls it Peaches and Cream. I doubt you could buy it now but I'll strike you a slip if you want one."

"I would love one, Mr Robbins." I sniffed the combined perfume of honeysuckle and rose and thought about Rosie, the new gypsy baby.

The day of the County Agricultural Show started with a breakfast fraught with phone calls. I was still not used to the number of people who telephoned between seven and eight o'clock with non-urgent queries. These early callers were surprised to find that they were not speaking to someone at the surgery. After the third such call, which I had answered with a screaming, kicking Clare under my arm, I strode back into the kitchen, dumped her on a chair and said to Peter, "do the patients really think we live at the surgery. Don't they think we sleep and eat like other humans?"

Peter shrugged, "you said it. They don't think."

"I would have thought the noises off were enough to convince them that I am not a white-coated receptionist standing with pencil poised," I muttered as I plonked a bowl of cereal in front of Clare. "Oh do be quiet." I suddenly yelled at her.

Peter looked at his watch. "It's eight o'clock. I can put the phone through to Dr Thomas now. He said he would take over at eight." Dr Thomas still liked to keep his hand in doing locum work. Peter went out of the kitchen to transfer the phone and suddenly the atmosphere in the house lightened. We were free; for a whole day we would not have to answer the telephone. We were going to The Show.

Peter pinned the Honorary Medical Officer's badge on to his lapel and we all got into the car to drive the half mile to the showground. The sloping field which was the Showground car park already had a shining crop of cars. Below were tents, marquees, flags and a fairground.

"I can see a helter-skelter," James yelled as we drove in through the main gate, able to avoid the miles of queuing traffic because of the emergency sticker on Peter's car.

"There's a big wheel as well," I pointed out feeling almost as childishly excited as they were. Peter parked outside the First Aid post and we all trooped in. The emergency services were in a row of ramshackle wooden huts. Firemen leaned against their engines in the early morning sunshine; policemen who had arrived for duty already looked hot in their navy uniforms and outside the First Aid Post elderly Red Cross ambulances were being manoeuvred into position. Peter disappeared into a room for a meeting with the other volunteer doctors.

"Come on, we want to go to the fair," the children pulled at my hands. Volunteer nurses, in the uniform of the Red Cross, smiled sympathetically as they walked past us adjusting their caps and aprons. Eventually Peter came out again.

"One of the other doctors is doing the first shift, so I'm free to look round until ten o'clock. Come on, let's go."

We set off up the main avenue of stalls. I promised to take the children to the fair when it opened later. We were all enthralled by the novelty of the show. There were stalls stocked with country clothes, stalls of furniture, cheap-jacks shouted from stalls where they demonstrated the latest and best-ever kitchen gadgets. As we passed the main ring an army band began to play a march; on all sides we could hear people, animals and music. A group of school children performed country dances on the 'village green' where blacksmiths, taking part in a shoeing competition, added the sounds of hammer on anvil.

"Balloons, look," Clare pointed. We looked up to see a flight of hot air balloons drifting overhead. Peter grinned at me.

"Life in the country isn't all work. Come on, let's go and look in the Flower Tent while it's not too busy."

The sides of the huge marquee were banked with flowers. Perfume from massed sweet peas, roses and carnations mingled with the smell of canvas and crushed grass. We walked around in silence at first, awed by the scale of each display, spires of delphiniums stood over begonia blooms of impossible size.

"Look at the roses," I breathed, as I stopped to admire a stand banked with perfect roses.

"How do they get vegetables like these?" Peter moved on to admire a kaleidoscopic design in tomatoes, corn cobs, cucumbers, frilly lettuces and scarlet peppers.

"Whew," I said when we stood for a moment outside the flower tent almost overcome by the steamy heat, the perfume and the size of everything.

"Coffee?" Peter suggested.

"Ice-creams," the children chorused, so we followed the signs to the refreshment tent. By the time Peter was due to go back to the First Aid hut, the sun had become very hot.

"I should think we'll be treating sunstroke and sunburn," he said as he left us, "see you in the Pavilion for lunch. Don't forget, we have to be there for one o'clock."

When he had gone we sat at the edge of the Main Ring to watch the display of heavy horses but the children soon grew restless.

"OK," I jumped up from the grass, "come on let's go to the fair."

To reach the fairground we had to cross one of the access points for the Main Ring. Stewards held the crowd back while the horses for the next display crossed the avenue on their way to the collecting ring.

"They don't like all the noise and the people," James said as one of the horses tossed its head. The rider pulled hard on the reins but the frightened horse reared, jerked his head again and managed to break away from his grip. There was a collective gasp from the crowd as the horse turned towards them; I grabbed the children's hands. We were at the back of the crowd so I was able to pull the children up a nearby bank of grass. We watched as men fought to recapture the runaway and regain control of a bunch of frightened horses. I saw a rider being helped to the edge of the crowd where he sat nursing his foot.

"Mummy, there's an ambulance coming," James pulled at my hand and pointed. "Do you think Daddy's in it?"

From our vantage point we could see as the crowds on the avenue, thick as ants, parted to let the ambulance through. To our disappointment, only a nurse and an ambulance man got out when the ambulance stopped.

"Never mind, it will be Daddy who sees what the rider has done to his foot back at the First Aid centre," I consoled the children when the crowd barriers were removed and we were able to continue on our way to the fair. They soon forgot everything but the magic of the fair. Above our heads people on the Big Wheel screamed with pleasurable fear and merry-go-round music mingled with the distant sound of a brass band. The air was thick with the smell of hot dogs and onions.

"What were the rider's injuries ?" I asked Peter over lunch in the canvas pavilion. Our folding chairs wobbled on the grass as we ate strawberries and cream.

"Only a bruised foot where the horse stood on him, though he was lucky it was nothing worse."

"Good job it was not one of the heavy horses," I said as I watched the VIP guests pass our table on their way to luncheon at the top table. The women, dressed as if for Ascot, teetered over the grass in their high heels, followed by Army Officers in dress uniforms.

"Top brass," Peter muttered into his strawberries. "I met some earlier."

"Weren't they friendly?"

"Umm I suppose so," Peter put on a mock upper crust accent, "got to be decent to the M O. Never know when you might need the chap don't y'know."

"Peter!" I nudged him. A very red-faced man was frowning at us from the far end of our table.

Refreshed by food and rest we went out into the sunshine and pushed our way through to the Food Fair.

"We should have come here before lunch," Peter groaned when he saw that the stall-holders were offering samples of sausages, oak smoked ham and ice-creams.

"You could fill up in here on samples," he muttered as we stared at stands selling exotic seafood, spices, smoked salmon and venison. We walked around and gazed at champion cheeses, beef carcases decorated with rosettes and prize-winning English wines.

"I could get indigestion just looking at all this," I said when we reeled out into the afternoon sun.

"I want to see the cows," Clare pleaded, so we walked to the cattle sheds and strolled past lines of tethered cattle in the cool straw-lined buildings. Clare was enchanted by the sight of bulls having their tails shampooed for the show ring. James found ginger-haired pigs and a breed of sheep which looked as if they just had perms for the show.

By the end of the afternoon we all felt as if we had walked miles. During his afternoon shift at the First Aid hut Peter treated sunburn and sunstroke as well as minor burns from chip frying and donut making.

"Visitors fell over tent guy ropes and twisted ankles in pot holes," he told me later, "they were stung by bees and butted by angry goats. Quite a variety. In fact," Peter said when we arrived back at the cottage, "it was like a busy casualty department on a summer afternoon!"

I groaned softly as I kicked my shoes off and sat down. "I enjoyed it all but I think I really prefer ordinary everyday life." Then the telephone started to ring.

"You do? Sure about that?" Peter said as he went to answer it.

He came back pulling his jacket back on.

"There's been an accident up on the railway line. The ambulance crew aren't sure if the victim was a stray animal or … " Peter picked up his bag." They want me to see if I can identify anything. Don't call me unless you have to. If it's urgent phone ambulance control. They'll have a vehicle there with a radio."

Bemused by the abrupt change from day-out to work I put two tired children in the bath.

The phone began to ring as soon as I had soaped them. For safety I hauled them out, protesting, on to towels.

"Is he there?" a voice demanded rudely. "I want to speak to the doctor."

Resisting the temptation to say "so do I," I replied evenly. "I'm sorry he's out at an emergency call."

"Well this is an emergency too," the insistent female voice went on. "My toilet won't flush."

I struggled with the temptation to tell her that Peter was a doctor, not a plumber.

"It's a health hazard, that's what it is," the caller said irritably. "I want the doctor to report it to the council. I've been ringing them all day but they haven't sent a plumber."

I recognised the voice as that of Mrs Black, one of our paranoid patients.

"I'm sorry but my husband is not here. You'll have to try ringing the council again in the morning."

"But what am I to do overnight?" The voice rose to the level of panic. I realised that the emergency was real enough to her.

"Throw a bucket of water down the loo," I advised, as I saw two naked children trailing wet towels down the stairs.

When Peter returned later he was grey-faced.

"Was it an animal?" I asked picturing the glossy prize winning creatures we had seen at the show.

"Peter shook his head as he sat down. "I'm sure it was a man. He must either have strayed on to the railway line or decided to commit suicide. A high speed train doesn't leave a lot for identification."

Silently I put the kettle on. As I got cups out of the cupboard there was a soft knock on the back door and I saw Mr Finch through the glass. He held out a freshly cut lettuce when I opened the door.

"I heard up the village that doctor's just been out to a nasty one." He shook his head, "never know from one minute to the next in this life do we? Never mind, life goes on, that's what I always say when I'm grave digging." his face brightened, "I thought you might like a lettuce." He turned and walked back to the gate as I called out my thanks. I looked at the lettuce in my hand and smiled at the speed with which news spread in the village. I closed the door on an eventful day.

# *Patients as People*

ONE EVENING IN EARLY JUNE we were off duty so I treated myself to a late walk on my own. The children were in bed and Peter was reading his way through the latest pile of professional journals and magazines which he calls his comics.

Along the lane silverweed was in full flower, its yellow cups almost hidden under silvery leaves. Out by the ford I saw Mrs Bailey filling a galvanised watering can at the water's edge. Her hanging baskets were set to soak in the brook.

"Nice evening, Mrs Stratford," Mrs Bailey called as she straightened up, her watering can dripping with brook water. "Garden's getting dry though," she added when she joined me on the footbridge where I leaned over to watch the water circling around the hanging baskets; lobelia floated in the gentle current as the moss soaked up water.

"Like to come and see the garden?" she asked, "Ted's got some lovely broad beans coming on."

I followed her over the footbridge. There was no boasting in her tone as there might be if she were offering to show me an expensive new washing machine.

Ted Bailey was hoeing between the beans. A tall angular man, he was so bent with arthritis that he used his garden tools to support himself while he worked.

"Doctor's wife's come to see your beans, Ted," Mrs Bailey said as she ran her watering can along a row of seedlings.

"Evening, Mrs Stratford," Ted leaned on his hoe so that he had a hand free to touch his cap.

"Good evening, Mr Bailey," I acknowledged his gesture with a smile as I surveyed the garden which would have done credit to a man half his age. "The beans look good."

"Time to take the tops out before they get the blackfly, here, Phyl," he called to his wife who had reached the end of the seed row, "will you take these tops out tomorrow?"

Mrs Bailey walked back towards us, the empty can dripping in her hand. "I'll nip them out just before dinner, go well with lamb chops they will. The peas aren't quite ready yet." She pulled two pea pods from the nearby row, handed one to me and opened the other to eat herself. The tiny peas were sweet.

"Too small to pick yet," Mrs Bailey lifted the leaves of the broad bean plants looking for pods. "Do you cook the bean tops when you pick them out, Mrs Stratford? They make a very tasty vegetable."

"I didn't even know you had to pick the tops out of broad beans," I admitted, "we are very new to gardening."

"Never mind, you'll learn," Mrs Bailey said comfortably. "Here look," she pinched the growing tip out of the nearest plant," go along your row and take the top out of every plant, you wont suffer from blackfly then."

"And I could cook these?" I took the bunch of bean leaves from her outstretched palm.

"Certainly you can, just boil them like spinach and you'll find them tender and tasty." Mrs Bailey picked a bean pod and opened it. Jade beans lay on the velvet lining. We ate them. "Too young yet," Mrs Bailey said, "we don't like them too big mind, when they get what we call black-eyed they are runchy, we like them just right." She smiled, "that means frequent sampling of course."

I thought of dieticians who exhort people to eat more vegetables and raw salads. Country gardeners, who would probably view cole-slaw with dismay, eat large amounts of raw garden produce as they sample the state of their crops.

"That's my lot for tonight," Ted pulled the weeds to one side with the blade of his hoe; then, using the handle as a walking staff, he began to make his way back to the path.

"Would you like to see our blackbird on her nest? he said as he negotiated the path between current bushes and thorny outstretched loganberry canes.

Mrs Bailey crossed the farmyard with us but went in through her kitchen door, leaving the watering can on the doorstep. I followed her husband to the side of the house where a pear tree grew almost up to the gable. With his finger to his lips Mr Bailey approached the tree. He parted the leaves. I peered in to find myself staring straight at the bright eye of the nesting bird. Silently we withdrew.

"Doesn't she mind?" I asked when we were back in the concrete yard which still radiated the heat of the day. "I would love to bring my children to see if you think she won't desert her nest."

Mr Bailey shook his head, "she won't desert. They're faithful mothers, you could take a hedge trimmer to that tree and she would sit tight until the last moment." He picked up the hoe which he had leaned against the wall of an open-fronted shed.

"What a treasure house," I exclaimed, peering inside.

He took this compliment seriously and began to point out objects to me, "those there are old ditching tools, don't have much call for they now, nor the old pitchfork and hay rake." His hand rested affectionately on the smooth wooden handles for a moment.

I looked up at the prize cards and rosettes pinned to a beam overhead, prizes from village flower shows with pre-war dates.

"If you like old things I'll show you something," Mr Bailey moved piles of clay flower pots so that he could reach the back of the shed. "Well, I'll be blowed," he pulled out a box of withered lily bulbs, "I been looking for these old jiggers ever since I put them away for their holiday last year. My wife says it's the first year she hasn't had lilies in the garden since we were wed." He looked up, "Ah that's what I'm looking for, up there by they rat traps." He reached up and unhooked a three legged stool full of worm holes. "Now then, do you know what this is? They fighting wood worms will have the legs off it soon."

"A milking stool."

"That's right. I made this for my wife, the morning we got married. We didn't have a honeymoon. In those days you didn't. We had the service, a slap-up meal at her place, then we had to come back here to milk the cows. She used her new stool."

I wondered what a modern bride would make of such a gift and an instant start to her chores. "Hard times?" I handed back the milking stool.

"Well," he thought about the question. "I suppose you might think so now but we didn't then. I remember my wife was milking two days before our first baby were born. All the men were busy haymaking you see. That old saying 'make hay while the sun shines' weren't said for fun, you had to take advantage of good weather. She left the heifers and the kickers for the men to milk but she did the rest," he said proudly, as he reached up to put the stool back on the hook where it would stay undisturbed for another fifty years.

"When I were a boy," he said staring into the past, "a woman used to come to father's farm to milk. She had a big family and her husband died young. We'd leave a pail out in the field and she'd be there before anybody else and have the pail full by six o'clock in the morning. Then she did the washing for mother and after that, while 'twas drying, she'd knit for us children." She bought a pig when she'd saved a bit," he added, " then a cow. Her eldest boy was killed in the war but she got a little farm together in the end. She were a hard working woman that one."

My new life as the doctor's wife suddenly didn't seem so hard after all. I had a brief premonition that I too would one day be remembering these as happy days.

"Well I must go home." Reluctantly, I ducked out of the low shed.

Mrs Bailey reappeared at her kitchen door with a bottle in her hand, "would you and the doctor care to try my elderflower cordial?" she handed me the bottle, cool from her dairy shelf.

"Bring the children out to see the blackbird any time you like," Mr Bailey said. "I'll be in presently, Phyl," he called as he opened the garden gate again, "I never 'noculated they punkins this afternoon, won't take me a minute. Cheerio, Mrs Stratford."

Mrs Bailey caught the puzzled look on my face. "his pumpkin flowers are more girls than boys so he has to 'noculate them by hand else we shan't have a heaviest pumpkin for the village show."

As I walked home in the twilight I looked forward to telling Peter about Mr Bailey's artificial insemination for pumpkins.

Along the lane it was almost dark under the full-leafed trees but the sky still had light enough for me to see that the bats were out hunting close to barns and houses which radiated heat stored from the day's sunshine. I turned into our gate feeling very mellow and contented.

We woke the next morning refreshed after a night without calls which was just as well since the day turned out to be anything but mellow. When Joan switched the telephone to me and warned me that trouble was brewing.

"I expect you will get a call from Mrs Butcher," she said primly; we both knew that the Mrs was an honorary title for the lady. Her neighbour was a fierce Baptist lay preacher called Mr Eden. The permanent state of war between these neighbours erupted sometimes into open conflict.

I was pegging out washing and watching Percy Coombes cutting the hay in the field beyond our wall when I heard the telephone ring. I ran in to answer it, shedding pegs along the path.

"I have rung the police and I want the doctor to come too." Mr Eden spluttered down the line. "She has gone too far this time, I shall get her put away. She should be in police custody or a mental hospital. The woman is not only bad she is mad!"

I had no need to ask who he meant. "I'm afraid my husband has already left surgery and gone in to the Cottage Hospital," I told him. As Mr Eden ranted I saw Clare pick up the pegs along the path. Brandy was stretched out asleep on the hot flagstones. I watched as Clare crept up to the cat, opening a peg between her small fingers. James was at school and she was bored.

"She poured slurry all over my garden gate," Mr Eden shouted in my ear, "what is that if it isn't the action of a mad woman?"

Brandy leapt in the air with an enraged shriek as Clare tried to put the peg on his tail. She came rushing indoors clutching a scratched arm and wailing loudly.

"Excuse me a moment, Mr Eden," I turned from the telephone." Go and turn the cold tap on and wash your arm until I can come and look." She fled into the kitchen.

"I don't really see what the doctor can do, Mr Eden," I turned my attention back to the telephone, "this is really a dispute between you and Mrs Butcher not a medical matter."

"He must come and give her something, the mad woman is still out there – listen." He held his receiver so that I could hear confused and distant sounds of mayhem in Cinnamon Lane.

"Alright, Mr Eden," I sighed, "I will ask my husband to call as soon as he can."

"I shall throw a bucket of water over her," he shouted as he put down the telephone. I thought the bucket of water would be more useful thrown over his manured gate but the line went dead so I never made the point. I walked through the kitchen door and saw Clare, standing on a chair at the sink, with the tap full on and water flowing over the edge of the sink.

"Pull the plug out!" I rushed towards her.

"I can't, it's stuck," she wailed.

By the time Clare and the kitchen were dry I knew it was one of those days. Peter came home for lunch in a rush because he had to return to finish the hospital round he had left to sort out Mr Eden and Mrs Butcher.

"When I wouldn't promise to admit Mrs Butcher to a psychiatric unit he wanted to get the vicar to exorcise her devils!" Peter groaned as he sat in front of a plate of hastily made sandwiches.

"I'll cook tonight, promise," I said guiltily, "it's been one of those mornings."

"You're telling me." Peter bit a sandwich in half. "I had twenty four people in surgery," the mouthful of sandwich muted his indignation. "I was late at the hospital, I missed seeing the consultant who had come to see one of my patients and then I had to go and sort out the Cinnamon Lane feud!"

"What did you do?"

"Sent the neighbours packing, cancelled the police car, told Mr Eden to hose his gate down and gave Mrs Butcher a tranquillizer." Peter sighed. "How can I tell an irascible, elderly, religious zealot that his neighbour is suffering from premenstrual tension, not possession by evil spirits!"

That afternoon Clare and I walked up Back Lane to collect James from school. Back Lane was part of the network of high-walled footpaths which thread through the heart of the village. At one point the footpath crossed a small allotment where an elderly man was busy hoeing between his rows of vegetables. He stopped to raise his ancient trilby to us and Clare ran over to talk to him. Reluctantly I soon had to call her to come on – we were going to be late at the school gate.

James was hot and cross when he came out of the school door, his shirt untucked, his hair stuck to his forehead and his satchel trailing on the playground.

"Come on, ice-lollies I think," I suggested to head off the thunder in his face. I bought three lemon ice-lollies at the village shop. As I paid for them I heard another Mum say loudly to a friend, "I thought they only ate health foods didn't you?"

I turned to smile and make some light comment but the hostile looks I got from the group of young mothers was colder than the lollies in my hand. Not for the first time I felt lonely. I missed the friendship of the mothers I had known before we moved to Northam. There I had been just Anne, not the doctor's wife. I had never understood the feelings of isolation expressed by the policeman's wife in our group. Now I knew how she felt. The children ran ahead with their lollies so I turned away and followed laden with shopping and James's bulging satchel. In Back Lane the high walls cast a cool shadow. Honeysuckle growing over the wall from a hidden garden smelled of summer and I could hear the distant hum of tractors at work in the hayfields. For a few moments I enjoyed the enclosed world, but when we reached the cottage I couldn't find my door key.

"You were playing with the keys, Clare," I said accusingly, as I scrabbled through the contents of my shopping basket and my pockets. Fright and tiredness made Clare start to grizzle.

"I only jangled them," she said, "when we were talking to that nice man in his garden."

"The allotment!" I sighed, "come on, back we go."

"I won't!" James sat on the doorstep and refused to move. I sympathised, he did look hot and tired but I could not leave him at the cottage alone. Stories of kidnapped children came to mind.

"I wouldn't go near the road," he pleaded.

"No James, I can't leave you here alone," I saw his mulish expression change and I turned to follow his eyes; a friendly face appeared over the wall.

"Afternoon," Percy Coombes tipped his cap to the back of his head, "Scorcher today isn't it?"

"I'd offer you a drink, Mr Coombes, but we're locked out," I told him. "The key was dropped in Back Lane, I'll have to go back and hunt for it." He looked at the drooping children.

"Fancy making a den in the bales do you?" he turned to me, "I'll keep an eye on them for a bit. They won't come to any harm making a house out of a few bales. The tractor isn't running just now. I'm waiting for my son-in-law to bring the trailer then we can start bale hauling. Like to help with the bales you two?"

"Yes please," James leapt to his feet, all trace of post-school weariness gone.

I walked back to the allotment where Mr Stratton, the gardener, was just clearing up to go home for tea.

"I never saw the little girl had any keys," he said with concern. We searched the long grass for half an hour, in the end I gave up.

"Thank you for looking, Mr Stratton, you go on home now, I must get back too. I can get the spare key from the surgery. If you do find them perhaps you'd let me or the doctor know?" I left him still looking round the edges of his compost heap and hurried through the village to the surgery.

The caravan was like an oven. Patients sat outside on waiting room chairs placed on the grass. They seemed happy to watch the builders making the foundations of the new surgery. Joan looked harassed and none too pleased to see me.

"It's difficult enough to run a surgery in this caravan without having the patients waiting in the garden!" she complained.

Peter was hot and tired too. He took his keys out and gave them to me when I slipped in to his room between patients. "Now I suppose I'll have to get a new set of keys cut." He sighed and looked longingly out of the caravan window. The builders, all stripped to the waist, were having a tea break under the trees in the old doctor's garden. Peter looked down at the notes piled on his desk and groaned, "constipation, piles and smelly varicose ulcers, just what I need on a day like this."

"You need a holiday. It's been hard for you since we moved here. Why don't you phone Dr Thomas?" I suggested," he loves coming back. We could get the old tents out and go somewhere for a short break. It would do you good. Go on, ask him."

"To come and work in an old gypsy caravan!"

"Ask him," I persisted, "he'd probably love it. Look I must go – I left the children in a hayfield."

"You what?"

"I'll explain later. Phone him," I said as I fled clutching the keys.

I let myself into the cottage, picked up my shopping and gathered the contents of James's satchel from the doorstep. From the kitchen window I could see Percy Coombes and his son-in-law stacking hay bales in the shaven field. I took Mrs Bailey's elderflower cordial from the fridge, made it up with cold water and poured it into a thermos which went into my emptied basket with spare mugs and a packet of biscuits. I would have a tin full of home-made cakes if I was a proper housewife, I thought as I locked the cottage door again and carefully stowed Peter's keys in my pocket.

The cut hay field was biscuit coloured. Where the ground rose to make a low horizon a heat haze shimmered as I walked towards the parked trailer.

"They're over there in the shade of the hedge," Percy Coombes called to me.

I waved the thermos, "a cool drink?"

He gave me a thumbs up so I turned and walked over towards the hedge. Bales had been stacked to make a little house of hay at the edge of the field. The silence of the afternoon was unbroken, even the birds were quiet. I got down on my knees in the prickly hay stubble to see Clare and James fast asleep in their hay house.

Percy and his son-in-law joined me. They grinned and made silent gestures

G.Younger

towards the sleeping children as they accepted my mugs of cold elderflower cordial. I got the impression that they were happy not to talk. Percy wiped his forearm across his sweaty brow and his shy son-in-law stared into his mug as they sat on spare bales. A jet from the nearby air-base suddenly ripped low across the sky sending shock waves of sound in all directions. The children sat up dazed with heat and sleep. Swiftly I poured their drinks to counter the shock of being woken. The plane was gone almost before we saw it.

"I don't know why them blamed things has to fly so low," Percy said as he handed back his mug, "enough to burst your eardrums. Terrifies the cows. Now then you two, these bales has got to be loaded, drink up." His bracing tone made them forget their fright and drain their mugs.

"Don't forget what I told you mind, never play near stacks of bales on your own, nor anywhere else on a farm. Dangerous places farms," he said as an aside to me.

"Thank you for letting them play out here, Percy," I said as I collected the mugs together. The children pushed the bales down so that Percy and his son-in-law could heave them on to the trailer. When the trailer was full we stood and waved as Percy drove the tractor away with his son-in-law sitting on the end of the trailer.

"The big boys at school were going bale-hauling, now I've done it," James said with pride in his voice. "We're proper now."

"I knew what he meant and felt that if the price of their country childhood was hard work for us and a measure of isolation it was worth every moment.

"Come on – tea-time, bath-time and phone-time," I said as we trailed back across the field. We climbed the wall into our garden. I looked back at the field, empty now of bales, and saw that the long uncut grasses at the field edge were pale as blonde baby hair against the sun.

"I phoned Dr Thomas," Peter said over supper when the children were in bed. "You were right, he is willing to be my locum for a few days so I've asked him to do next Friday, the weekend and Monday so we can take the tent and go off for a long weekend while the weather holds."

"Good," I was about to say more when the doorbell rang.

"Oh who's that?" Peter sighed and went out to the hall.

"Your wife's keys, doctor."

I followed Peter and saw Mr Stratton on the doorstep. He was wearing his best suit with a boiled shirt ironed to perfection. His face, freshly shaved, smiled as he held out the missing keys. "Under the raspberries. I found them when I went to pick some for the wife's tea." With his other hand he offered a punnet of raspberries. We were in the middle of our thanks when the telephone began to ring.

"Sounds like work for you, doctor," Mr Stratton lifted his hat, "good evening."

"You know," Peter said as he picked up his case, "the trendy lefties would have a fit at gestures like that, they'd probably rabbit on about subservience and feudalism."

I went back inside to clear the supper things smiling to myself. As I washed up I watched the pair of nesting swallows swooping in and out of our stone garden shed.

Later, when Peter came back, he let himself in. I went to the kitchen to make coffee and found him washing his hands at the sink.

"What was the call?" I asked as I handed him a towel. Grinning, he dried his hands and pulled his shirt sleeves down.

"Mr Eden from this morning's problem in Cinnamon lane went to supper with the chairman of the Gardening Club this evening. When he complimented his hostess on the pork casserole she told him it was a pork and cider casserole!"

I frowned, "So?"

"The man is fanatically anti-alcohol. He's now got raging indigestion brought on by the conviction that he has sinned!"

We got up early on the day of our long weekend off. When we had packed the camping equipment into the car there was hardly room left for us and the children. Their excitement was infectious. I was sad to leave the swallows and the garden but Peter was light-hearted as a boy let out of school. The road to Devon was quiet in the early morning sun but few miles from our destination we drove around a bend and saw an accident ahead. Peter pulled up quickly.

"Stay in the car," he said tersely to the children who stared from the back seat. "Don't move until we come back."

We ran to the nearest car where an elderly man in the driver's seat clutched his forehead. Blood ran through his fingers. Gently Peter moved his hand and to my utter horror I saw that his eye socket was empty. I had never liked dealing with eye injuries. The driver of the other car – a large and expensive one which had apparently shot out of a side turning – was blustering and complaining about the damage to his car.

"Go and telephone for an ambulance," Peter said sharply. The man glared but set off down the lane.

"I'm quite all right," our patient said quietly, "I only bumped my head on the windscreen."

"Your eye … " Peter began.

"It's in my pocket," the elderly man struggled and put his hand in his pocket from where he produced a glass eye. "Lost it in the war you know." He smiled sweetly at us. "I only wear it on special occasions and I am on my way to a wedding."

I stifled my gasp of surprise and relief. Peter introduced himself as a doctor and checked the gentleman's pulse.

"You are very kind doctor," he said gently, "but I really am all right you know. This is nothing compared to the war!"

When the police and an ambulance arrived to take charge of the situation we went back to our car. The children still sat, large eyed and silent, as we had left them.

"Is the man all right, Daddy?" James asked.

Peter grinned at me as he turned the ignition, "yes, he's going to be all right and we are going on holiday right now!"

The holiday was mixed as holidays so often are, some sunshine and a good dose of rain when we were confined to a tent with two bored children. We had looked forward to sleeping at night without a telephone in earshot but we were not undisturbed.

"I wish people would remember that tents are not soundproof," Peter grumbled one night when we were trying to get to sleep with pop music from the tent on our left and an argument being conducted loudly in the tent on our right.

"Umm," I agreed, "when you can't settle the ground suddenly seems lumpier doesn't it?" I was beginning to long for my own bed. By midnight we were losing patience. The last straw was when both children got up.

"We can't sleep," a cross and sleepy James came to act as spokesman. I crawled out of my sleeping bag.

"I'll come and see," I wrapped a travel rug around my shoulders as I said to Peter, "I think you'll have to go next door and ask them to shut up. It is after midnight."

Peter sighed and I saw the look which I recognised as his night call expression, a combination of weariness and resignation.

He stumbled outside as I followed James to the children's small tent where Clare was wide-awake. I heard a muttered yelp followed by barking and grimaced as I guessed that Peter had disturbed the dog sleeping under the fly-sheet of the tent next door. Then there was silence.

"OK folks bedtime." Peter said.

I got the children snuggled down in their sleeping bags before I backed out of their tiny tent on all fours.

As I humped myself into my sleeping bag I whispered, "back to the telephone?"

"See you in the morning after a lie-in," Peter mumbled as he pulled his sleeping bag round his ears and instantly fell asleep.

The lie-in never happened. We were woken at five-thirty by shrieks from the children's tent. Peter poked his nose out of his sleeping bag but left me to investigate. Early calls on holiday were my job it seemed.

I unlaced the tent flap and peered outside. Heads were appearing from other tents to see what was going on. James and Clare's tent was collapsing with the children peeping out of the ruins.

Breathless with giggles James shouted, "Mummy these two heifers have knocked our tent down."

Two skittish young heifer calves were investigating the half collapsed tent. Peter crawled out beside me to peer, bleary-eyed, at the early morning entertainment.

"They must have got in through that gap in the hedge," he said as he crawled outside. I followed, wincing as the wet grass bathed my bare feet. Peter advanced on the heifers, with his arms outstretched, using the herding shouts learned from our local farmers and a few of his own invention, "woa, garn there, mush." I approached from the opposite direction. We succeeded in herding the two animals back through the hedge. Peter pulled some brushwood down to fill the gap. We turned to go back to our tent to see that a small audience had gathered to watch. As Peter pulled up the guy ropes of the children's tent a lad in pyjamas came over to help. He was the midnight pop music fan.

"Are you a farmer?" he asked.

Peter shook his head. Away from home, he is always reluctant to admit to his profession. "No but we live in the country."

"I wouldn't have tackled them," the man from the next tent admitted as he hammered the children's tent pegs firmly in place with a stone. I guessed that he had been part of the noisy midnight argument.

"Oh you get used to things like that," Peter said airily.

"They were only little heifers," James added with all the knowledge of his short rural experience.

"Well I wouldn't trust them," our neighbour said, glaring through the hedge at the heifers butting an old nurse cow for their breakfast. "At this time of the morning too." He stumped back towards his tent.

"Best time of the day," Peter rubbed his hands together as if he was enjoying the dawn like a true countryman. "I'll put the kettle on."

We stayed our planned time at the campsite and returned refreshed for the change of scene but glad to be back home.

As soon as I had all the holiday washing on the line I escaped for a walk. Peter was not back on duty so we were telephone-free for a few more hours. I walked out to the ford and leaned on the footbridge from where I could see Mr Bailey's garden. It was good to be home. I breathed in the smell of farmyard and river.

"Over here," a hidden voice called. I crossed the footbridge and opened the gate into the farm's kitchen garden. Mr Bailey sat on an upturned oil drum in the middle of the fruit bushes with his walking stick between his knees.

I pushed through heavily laden blackcurrant bushes.

"Try some of my Golden Drops," he leaned forward to hook a branch of the nearest gooseberry bush with the curled end of his walking stick.

"There, help yourself," he held the branch up for me with his stick. The gooseberries were transparent golden globes which exploded on my tongue.

"I always thought gooseberries were sour," I exclaimed reaching for another.

Mr Bailey shook his head, "not if you leave them long enough. They're like good people – they get better with age." He heaved himself to his feet, "you can borrow a basket from the kitchen and fill it for the family if you like." I followed his slow steps back through the garden. Mr Bailey smiled cheerfully as he turned to close the gate behind us, "I went to see Dr Thomas this morning. First time I've been to the doctor's in a caravan. Very pleasant it was sitting outside waiting in the sunshine. A bit hot inside, but homely. Now you come and see my tomatoes."

Mr Bailey's greenhouse, a lean-to over the backdoor to the farm kitchen, was dripping with recent watering and hot with the smell of tomatoes and geraniums.

"I gave they too much oh-be-joyful," Mr Bailey said shaking his head over his elongated tomato plants. Seeing my puzzled expression he explained, "I put too much yard muck in the greenhouse dirt, now they tomatoes is racing to Jericho."

Stepping over two cats asleep in the sunny doorway he reached a small basket from a kitchen shelf.

"There – go and help yourself. The doctor will enjoy them. Good for the bowels gooseberries."

I walked home with my basket full of Golden drops past the orchard where adolescent calves stood knee deep in flowering grasses; some stood in the river cooling their legs in the shade of the willow over the wash pool. Swallows courted on the telegraph wires along the lane. Mr Bailey had told me that his father always left the door to the hayloft open after April for the annual return of the swallows.

# *Sow escapes!*

"CAN YOU TAKE OLD WALT Ford's tablets to him this afternoon?" Peter asked one summer lunch time. "Apparently his knee is so bad he can't get up to the surgery and I thought as he only lives a few doors away - "

"All right, I'll go." I tried to sound put-upon but Peter knew very well that I liked an excuse to call on patients. I envied his freedom to enter people's homes.

I put the tablets and a bunch of white roses in a basket. Old countrymen are not bashful about flowers. They still wear buttonholes in their lapels, give bunches of garden flowers away and like to receive them in return.

"Hello, Mr Ford, I've brought your tablets," I called into the open cottage door. The children hung behind me on the path.

"I'm here," he growled and I turned to see Mr Ford limping from his outside lavatory. He left the door wide open and I caught a glimpse of white-washed walls, a polished wooden lavatory seat and sheets of torn newspaper on a wall hook.

"Got to leave the door open to let the stink out, he glared at me. "What did you say you come for?"

"I've brought your tablets and these," I held the roses out. He took them and sniffed, "smell's better than in there," a mischievous smile turned up the corners of his mouth. "Put your basket on the step. You might as well see the garden now you're here."

"How's your knee?"

"Pains I cruel," he said dismissively as he stopped on the path, "there did you ever see better begonials than they?"

We stopped by one of the many plant containers outside his back door. Huge scarlet and orange pendulous begonias hung over the edge of a soil-filled tractor tyre. Nasturtiums climbed out of china lavatory pans by the coal house door and petunias grew in galvanised baths. More tractor tyres ablaze with marigolds and busy lizzies flanked the path. I resisted the temptation to get my sun-glasses out as Old Walt's taste in primary colours dazzled my eyes.

"I can't bend down to tend flowers in the ground now so I grows 'em like this," Walt said poking a clay pot of geraniums with his walking stick.

"You've got a fine show in the ground though," I said resting my eyes on the cottage pinks which grew under the garden walls.

Walt grunted, "fend for themselves they do, I don't cosset they." He stopped beside a patch of laced pinks, "some of the best blossoms come from a hard life." He stumped on down the path and stopped by a bed of deep violet-blue flowers. "You want some of these bell-flowers for your garden? I'll break off a bit in the autumn."

I began to protest about his arthritis but he ignored me and went on, "don't you spoil them mind, these grow where I empty the ash pan every day in winter. Treat them too soft and they'll sulk like spoilt children." He glared at James and Clare from under his bushy eyebrows. To my surprise I could see that they were not at all disconcerted by him.

"Want to make yourselves useful?" he said to them in a tone which invited no refusal. "Here then," Walt picked up a punnet from the pile of orange boxes and old wooden seed boxes piled by his garden shed. "Take this down to the bean row and pick enough beans for my dinner tomorrow and some for your mother to take home. And don't pull the bines," he growled after them as they ran off down the path towards the bean row at the end of the garden.

As the children squatted on the soil to peer under the bean leaves I felt free for a moment to enjoy myself.

"Did you build this, Mr Ford?" I put a hand on the hot, tarry-smelling timbers of his garden shed. "It's massive."

"That's an old linesman's shed that is," Walt put his shoulder to the sliding door to show me how it ran in metal tracks. "Old Dr Beeching didn't get everything when he took our railway from us. Forty years I worked on the railway, I reckoned I was entitled to a bonus or two." A grin lit up his old face, "see these sleepers?" he poked the path with his stick, "you keep your eyes open and you'll see plenty of paths like this round the village."

"And your bungalow?" I said as I shaded my eyes and looked at his wooden home properly for the first time.

"Ah now, that come from army surplus, not the railway. My Dad brought he back in the 20's after the Great War. Temporary barrack block for some of they poor beggars who ended up in the trenches that was. Dad borrowed a Scammell lorry from one of the quarries and fetched him back here." His grin widened, "Dad couldn't drive, mind, but he had plenty of time to learn between here and Salisbury. Roads was quiet in them days."

I thought of some of the high-speed road accidents that Peter attended.

"Was life better in those days?"

Walt lowered himself on to the old wooden bench under his kitchen window.

"Depends what you mean by better?" He indicated that I should sit down beside him. "Life were quieter. The village never had many incomers so you knew everybody but it weren't better in your husband's line of business. My wife died in childbirth like plenty of others." He gazed down the garden where my children were still searching for beans. "In my mother's day," he went on, "a child caught her dress on fire up the school, they had open fires then, and there weren't no ambulance to send for. They thought about sending for the vicar but you didn't bother he with things like that. She died that night."

In spite of the heat of the sun I shivered at the thought of the child's pain.

"Great invention these new pain-killers," Walt took the bottle I had bought him out of his trouser pocket. "My Dad were that twisted up with arthritis in the end he couldn't turn himself over in the bed. He'd have given his right arm for pills like these. No, they weren't really better days."

The children came running along the path, scattering beans from the overflowing punnet. "Tip a few in there," Walt ordered, pointing to a blue-edged enamel washing up bowl on his back step. "Keep the rest for your mother, she's got more to feed than I have." He heaved himself to his feet. "Any time you're passing come in," he said to me, "and if you want I'll look after these rascals." The children grinned at the prospect of Mr Ford as a child-minder. "Don't you think you could make a riot," he shook his stick at them, "just because I can't run about, doesn't mean I can't keep a pair of children in order."

I picked up my basket, now full of runner beans. "Thank you, Mr Ford. I'll remember that. If you want any shopping from Moreton any time just let me know. Thank you for the beans."

Back in my kitchen I was slicing beans when Joan rang to transfer the phone at the end of evening surgery.

"Doctor will be late home," she said sombrely, "he's been called out to an accident."

"A road accident?"

"No, a home accident of some sort, I don't quite know what had happened, a young woman rushed into surgery just now in a terrible state, she said her neighbour's child had been hurt."

"Oh dear," I looked over from the phone to the half-prepared beans on the draining board. "You go home then, Joan, I'll look after the calls now." I put the phone down, finished the beans and put them in a pan to await Peter's return. I was reading *Wind In The Willows* to the children in bed by the time I heard Peter's car.

I went down the stairs as he let himself in the front door. He put his case down as if it was full of lead.

"Supper?"

He nodded silently and watched as I put the beans on to cook.

"It was a pushchair," he said suddenly as he leaned on the edge of the sink to stare out of the kitchen window. "A toddler, parked under a tree in her pushchair to sleep in the heat of the afternoon, her Mum inside ironing. The child must have woken up. The catch slipped, the pushchair folded up on her and the handle broke her neck."

"Poor child, ... " I began.

"Daddy," an indignant voice from upstairs called, "you haven't said goodnight to us."

Peter stood up and took a deep breath. "I'll go and tuck them in."

I prodded the boiling beans, checked the chops under the grill and thought of Mr Ford's story of the village child who died of burns so long ago.

The next afternoon I picked raspberries under a darkening sky. Thunder rumbled around the hills. The air was heavy.

"I don't like that noise," Clare said uncertainly.

I looked up at the bruised sky. "There's going to be a storm any minute. You go and find Brandy and shut him in. He wont like the storm either. I have to finish picking these raspberries so that we can make jam." As I picked from the last canes in the raspberry row huge drops of rain splashed on the path. The smell of hot stone rose as the rain hissed down. I picked up my pan-full of fruit and ran for the back door. Lightning forked over the cut fields.

In the kitchen I washed the fruit and assembled my jam-making equipment. Rain was sluicing down the windows and I was glad of an occupation; the death of a child had stunned the village and we all felt depressed.

Jam-making on duty did not prove to be easy. Once the sugar was in the bubbling raspberries I had to keep stirring to stop them burning. But the telephone did not quite stretch over to the stove. Some afternoons were quiet but this was not one of them. Perhaps the storm and yesterday's news is upsetting everybody, I thought as I put down the telephone at the end of another non-urgent call.

"Is it ready yet?" James called from the hall where they were making a den to keep them away from the boiling jam.

"Not quite." I spooned another sample of the jam onto a saucer to test it for setting. The pool of jam wrinkled at the edges when I poked it with my finger. I gave the preserving pan contents another stir, turned the heat off and lifted a tray of hot jars out of the oven when the doorbell rang.

"Damn!" I went out into the hall.

"Mind our house," an aggrieved voice shouted as I pushed past a fragile structure of cardboard boxes and sheets draped over my clothes airer. I opened the door to find Mr Finch on the doorstep.

"Come inside," I pulled the startled sexton into the hall where his oilskins shook rain all over the den.

"Hey, it's raining," James and Clare looked out from under the sheets. "Hello Mr Finch."

"Sorry about that," Mr Finch looked bemused.

"Come in here, Mr Finch," I said hurriedly returning to my jam. "Sorry but I can't stand talking on the doorstep. This jam is about to set."

"My wife's doing just the same." He stood dripping on the lino tiles.

"Hang your coat over there," I indicated the hook on the backdoor, "it can drip on the doormat then." I began to pour the jam into the rapidly cooling jars. "What can I do for you Mr Finch?"

"I bought this for the doctor." He took a package out of his wet coat, "it's a special type of bolt for one of the surgery doors. Saves me walking all the way up there on an afternoon like this. You don't mind?"

"Of course not," I wiped long drips of jam from a jam jar.

"Nasty business about the little girl," Mr Finch shook his head. "Can't say as I look forward to that funeral. I hate digging children's graves, not that I have to that often these days, thank the Lord."

I put the tops on the jam jars. "How about a cup of tea, Mr Finch?"

"Never say no to that." He watched me as I put the kettle on. "Years ago, when a child died, the women used to line the grave with flowers. That hid the earth so's you didn't look down into such a black hole. I heard up the village this morning," he went on, "all that poor mother keeps saying is 'she was afraid of the dark.'"

My hand stopped on its way to pick up the tea pot. "We must organise it then Mr Finch," I clasped the teapot to my apron and turned to face him.

"Organise what?"

"The flowers, like they used to have. The gardens are full of flowers at this time of year. You put the word around and tell us when to come and we'll do it."

"I'll have to ask the vicar," he said uncertainly, "and the undertaker."

I poured his tea and put the mug in front of him. "It's a deal then?"

I didn't go to the funeral. I stayed to answer the telephone while Peter went.

"Was it harrowing?" I said when he came back.

"Yes. But the flowers in the grave helped. Some of the florist's efforts were a bit gaudy, you know, Teddy Bears made of yellow chrysanthemums," he shrugged "but some people like that sort of thing. The garden flowers in the grave looked good though. A sort of tapestry effect."

"Any news on the building front?" I asked to cheer him up.

"Oh, yes, I forgot to say, the roof trusses arrive tomorrow. We should be in by September."

"So you can start the winter in your brand new surgery, great." The telephone began to ring. "I'll get it." I went out to the hall, answered the telephone and came back frowning. "It was Sister in casualty at the Cottage Hospital, she said she's got a "Come-On-Johnny" elbow for you. What on earth is that?"

Peter let out a yelp of laughter. "You did a casualty job didn't you? It's a well known one that. Mum or Dad gets fed up with little Johnny who is probably whining and certainly hanging back when they are in a hurry to get somewhere, they give his arm a yank as they mutter, 'Come on Johnny,' and dislocate his elbow." He got up from his chair and pulled his coat back on. "Shouldn't be too hard to put back in place."

He went off looking happier. Like a lot of men Peter can cope with a practical problem much better than an emotional one.

"Joan's got the telephone now," he shouted as he went out to the car. "You take the children out for a walk if you want. Blow the cobwebs away."

The storms had stopped but water was pouring from the field drains. At the ford the brook water ran brown and muddy across the roadway. The ducks were sailing in flotilla under the footbridge as we arrived at the water's edge.

"I've brought some tea for you ducks," James shouted as he began to empty his pockets of crusts. His overarm bowling was so enthusiastic that he lost his footing, slipped on the algae covered stones and did a belly flop into the water. As he came up dripping and crying Mr Bailey appeared on the footbridge.

"There now," he said as he helped me to pull my wet son to the bank, "you've been christened."

James stopped crying.

"Every good Northam lad has to be christened in the brook at least once you know," Mr Bailey's tone was matter-of-fact. "Come on let's see what Mrs Bailey can find for you to wear in place of those wet things."

James followed Mr Bailey, his wet sandals squelching at every step.

Clare followed. "Do I have to be christened?" she whispered to me.

"No," I assured her quickly looking over the footbridge rail at the water. It was only inches deep, even in flood, but dangerous enough. "You've been christened properly in a church."

"Wasn't James?"

"Yes," I whispered as we crossed the farmyard. "Mr Bailey just wanted to make James feel better about falling in the water."

When we reached the porch over the kitchen door James had already disappeared upstairs with Mrs Bailey.

"Here," Mr Bailey reached down a tennis ball and gave it to Clare, "you throw that for th'old dog. Mind the gravy from the muck heap, all that rain has set the heap running."

The farm dog, which had been asleep outside the back door, lumbered to his feet and looked hopeful.

"He's old and quiet," Mr Bailey assured me as Clare trotted out to the centre of the yard to throw the ball. I glanced up to see where the ball had been stored and saw that in the space between the laths of the porch roof and the door lintel there was a convenient shelf for old tennis balls, paint brushes, trowels, and other small garden tools.

"That's a handy place," Mr Bailey said following my gaze. "On the way to the garden I can just reach down a dibber or a trowel."

Not for the first time I wished that I could draw or paint. The handy shelf displayed a real country collection; unlike the artfully arranged dried flowers or herbs hung to dry from cottage beams in trendy kitchens.

James came down the stairs followed by Mrs Bailey.

"These belonged to Mrs Bailey's own boy," he told me proudly, "and he was christened in the river too."

He was attired in old navy shorts, an Aertex shirt, knee-length socks and plimsolls of antique design. Mrs Bailey had his wet clothes in a bag for me. I was thanking her when we all heard the sound of shouting and the clanging of metal.

"That'll be Tommy," Mr Bailey turned to the door, "I told he to move that sow."

We all went outside to see Tommy, Mr Bailey's elderly farm-hand, in the yard brandishing a sheet of corrugated iron like a shield at a large saddleback sow. The pig was trying to run towards the brook. Tommy banged on his rusty shield with keys from his pocket as he bellowed "ha, yah," at the confused sow.

"You children stand there," Mr Bailey stationed James and Clare in the farmhouse door, "stretch your arms out and make noises if she comes this way." Mr Bailey brandished his stick as he joined Tommy to head the sow towards a small gate, her trotters skidding on the yard stones.

"Always was a comical pig that one," Mrs Bailey said from behind us as we watched the antics in the yard. "I suppose you'd say awkward maybe, but we say comical. Tommy's trying to get her into the old orchard," she explained, "she's constipated and there's nothing like a bit of fresh grass for that."

Tommy beat a tattoo on his piece of corrugated iron, Mr Bailey followed with his stick and the children rushed across the yard, flailing outstretched arms and imitating Tommy's cries of "hah, yah," at full volume. When the sow had settled in the orchard we leaned on the gate to watch as magpies came to share the pig's insects. I wondered if Peter could prescribe fresh grass to his many constipated patients!

Over supper later I told him the story to cheer him up.

"Sounds more fun than evening surgery was," he sighed. "It was all about babies; patients who don't want the baby they are expecting, patients who want a baby and can't conceive one, patients with too many who want to be sterilized and to top it all, at nearly seven o'clock when I thought I'd come to the end, a couple who don't know how to do it at all."

"You mean … ?"

"An unconsummated marriage. Sort that one out in ten minutes at the end

G.Younger

of surgery!" He ran his fingers through his hair," your sow sounds easier to handle."

I grinned, "well, as she was enormously pregnant I don't think she had that problem. She's due to farrow any day and Mr Bailey has promised to let me know. I'm going to take the children to watch if it's a reasonable time of day."

"Best way for them to learn," Peter yawned, "I reckon country practice is great for our children; I'm not so sure about us." The telephone began to ring and he groaned softly as he went to answer it.

"A girl with tummy ache," he said briefly as he picked up his jacket. "Sounds like she's eaten too many strawberries or could be an appendix I suppose."

"How old is she?" I started to clear the table.

"Fifteen. You know her, she's the plump girl who sometimes helps in the shop on Saturdays. I shouldn't be too long."

"I'll make some coffee when you get back," I said, but I had coffee on my own. By nine o'clock I had given up waiting for Peter to join me. It was ten o'clock when I heard his car return. I got up and went through to the kitchen to make fresh coffee.

"Not too many strawberries?"

He shook his head, "I should have guessed after all the other things in surgery today. An undiagnosed pregnancy she had managed to hide from everyone including her mother!"

"She is a big girl," I said as I filled the kettle. "Have you sent her to the maternity unit then?"

"Too late for that," Peter took his jacket off and pulled his tie loose. "I got there just in time to deliver the infant. An undernourished baby girl but OK. I left Nurse Jackson in charge."

"Oh, she'll be in her element." I handed Peter a mug of coffee, "she was only lamenting the lack of home deliveries to me the other day when I met her outside the caravan. Mavis's baby was her only home delivery this year, now she's had two."

Peter gulped some coffee, "in what she calls "the good old days", two a week wouldn't have been unusual."

"What a lot of night calls that must have made."

"For her, yes, don't forget then a midwife only called the doctor if she thought things weren't progressing as they should. Now midwives have been pushed to the sidelines as doctor's helpers." Peter looked ruminatively into his coffee, "I think it's a shame. Mums like to have midwives."

"And midwives like Nurse Jackson miss the drama."

Peter grinned. "Well she had a bit tonight. The girl's family were in total shock. As soon as I saw what was going on I got them to phone her. She came like the cavalry in an old film, ready to save the day.

"Boiling kettles and all that stuff? Film scriptwriters always seem to think that quantities of boiling water are required for childbirth.

"Oh, it was real make-do and mend stuff," Peter said, "old towels cut up for nappies and a crib made up in a dresser drawer. You're right, Nurse Jackson was in her element."

The next morning I had a phone call to announce another imminent delivery.

"Mrs Stratford? Mr Bailey. Remember that old comical pig, well she's farrowing. I promised to let you know so's you could bring the children."

"We'll be there right away. Oh, where Mr Bailey?" I remembered to ask.

"Up the track by the side-gate, you know, where the styes are. She's in the farrowing pen. You'll hear us, I daresay. Be quick mind."

The children, who had been crayoning in a bored and desultory way, were out in the lane before I had the door locked. We ran to the farm and out to the styes where Mr Bailey was leaning on the door of the farrowing pen. Inside I could see Tommy on his knees beside the sow, who lay on her side panting.

"Just in time," Mr Bailey lifted James up and I heaved Clare up to see over the pen door.

"There look," Mr Bailey pointed as the third piglet slipped out and Tommy laid it on the straw beside its siblings.

"They're like tiny pink silk parcels." I exclaimed as more piglets followed fast.

"I want to hold one," Clare demanded but Mr Bailey said, "not yet. They want to get to the milk bar first look."

Tommy placed the row of piglets by the sow's teats.

"See, they know what to do, don't 'um." Tommy grinned, 'tis nature you see."

We did see. The children were entranced. No film they would ever watch in a biology lesson could compete with the reality of that birth, the smell of hot pig, the sheen of newness on the piglets and their expressions of bliss when they were suckling. My arms ached so I put Clare down. Mr Bailey put

James down too. As they protested he said, "want to come and feed some calves?"

We all took a turn at bucket-feeding the calves who had huge eyes and knobbly knees.

"Like this," Mr Bailey showed me how to put my fingers into the bucket of milk to guide the calves down to drink. As the little heifer calf found my fingers she sucked hard.

"Oh, her tongue is like sandpaper," I exclaimed. Mr Bailey held another bucket for the children to feed a tiny black bull calf. Soon the low-beamed dusty old calf pen was full of laughter, the smell of milk and the sound of suckling.

"You look in the orchard on your way back home," Mr Bailey said when he washed the empty buckets in a trough of rainwater outside in the yard. "There's a nurse cow in the old orchard. She's a rare good step-mother she is. You go and see."

The children ran ahead of me back to the lane and climbed the orchard gate; I joined them.

"She must have gallons of milk," James said with awe. The nurse cow was a bony gaunt old cow with a white fringe, where her horns had been disbudded, between black hairy ears. On her full udder hung three calves, one under her tail facing forward and two at her side with their tails switching their patient nurse's muzzle. As the calves sucked vigorously bubbles formed at the corners of their mouths and milky dribble fell into the grass. Suddenly she lost patience with them and decided to walk towards the water trough to get a drink for herself. For a moment all three calves hung on to her udder, two walking backwards and the one at the rear trying to keep up. But her thirst was too great and she swung away from them to dip her head deep into the water trough.

"Come on, time to go home now," I jumped down from the five-barred gate. "They've all had elevenses. It's time we went back home, I've got letters to type for the surgery and Daddy will want lunch soon." On the way back to the cottage I wondered if Peter's patient from the night before was feeding her baby and what the child's future was. For the first time I was struck by the thought that we might see the child grow up. Peter might even deliver her child one day. Country practice has its drawbacks, I thought, but it has its compensations too.

❧ ❧ ❧

# *Summer Time*

WE WERE TRYING TO GET to sleep on a hot night in late summer. Even with all the windows open our bedroom was airless. The telephone began to ring. Peter flung off the sheet and rolled over to pick it up. I half sat up to turn my pillow to the cool side and heard shouting from the receiver in Peter's hand.

"Bats," I heard a panic-stricken female voice shouting, "my husband was trying to get them out. He stubbed his toe, I think he's broken it." Banging and howls of pain echoed down the telephone.

Peter scribbled down the address, put the receiver down and got up to dress.

"One old doctor I knew used to go out to calls with his jacket over his pyjamas," he muttered as he pulled his trousers on, "he said it made the patients realise that they had got him out of bed."

"Cold in the winter," I sat up bleary-eyed. "Anyway you never wear pyjamas. You'd look silly with a jacket over your birthday suit, even in this weather!"

I reached for a book to read when Peter had gone. I knew if I fell asleep he would wake me when he got back into bed, then I would be back to tossing and turning in the heat. I began to read. Small sounds attracted my attention – too late I remembered that I had put the light on with the windows open. The bedroom was full of moths. Big furry moths blundered into the lampshade and fell on to the bedspread. I dived under the sheet and stayed there until I heard Peter come up the stairs.

"What are you doing?" he asked when he came into the bedroom to find me reading by torchlight under the sheet.

"Moths, big ones, get them out."

Peter flapped around the room with a medical magazine. I heard him score some hits.

"Don't kill them," I peered out from under the sheet.

"Well what do you want me to do?" he asked in exasperated tones, "ask them if they would leave the room?" He swept up another furry body up on a page lurid with photographs of diseased genitals, shook the moth out of the window and pulled the catch with a bang.

Peter sat down on the bed to pull his socks off. "I saw a badger in my headlights just now, trundling down the lane."

"Lucky you, I only ever see squashed ones," I peered out from under the sheet, "is it safe to come out now?"

"You're as bad as the couple I've just been to see."

"Yes, what was going on there?"

Peter smiled as he rolled into bed. "They'd had all their windows open like us and two bats flew in."

"I thought bats had such wonderful sonar systems they didn't make mistakes like that?"

"Well these two did." Peter pounded his pillow into shape. "The wife was hysterical. Her husband had been rushing round the room with a newspaper trying to get the bats to fly out of the window. Apparently he had a sheet of newspaper on his head in case a bat flew into his hair. A corner of the paper flopped down over his eyes, he ran into the corner of a chest of drawers and I think he has broken one of his toes. He had a big toe like a burst plum."

"Ouch, poor man." I put my torch out as I snuggled down imagining the pain of the stubbed toe.

Peter began to laugh softly. "the funny thing was, like me he doesn't wear pyjamas and there he was protecting his head with a newspaper. I'd have thought he might have protected a more vital area. Just think," he curled up with mirth, "bats on your balls!"

When Joan took over the telephone the next day I took the children down the lane past Mrs Lee's bungalow. As usual she was out in the garden and pleased to see us.

"Hello darlins," she opened the gate to let the children in. I got somethin' to show you two." Mrs Lee took their hands and flapped along the path in her old felt slippers. I followed behind.

"There now," she stopped as we rounded the bungalow. Standing in the paddock was a short-legged, barrel shaped Shetland pony.

"Can we ride him?" Clare immediately asked."

Mrs Lee shook her head sadly with a significant look in my direction. "You ain't got no bumpin' hats. What would your Father say to me if you fell off his back and broke your heads open."

"We wouldn't, we wouldn't," they chorused, glaring at me, although I had not spoken.

"He needs shoeing anyway," Mrs Lee said to placate them. "Costs me £10 to have that little old pony shod. Terrible I say that is." She smiled in my direction. "I had a chap from Australia stop by here the other day. Used to be a blacksmith's apprentice in the village he did. What a remembrance he got on him. He could tell I things I'd forgot. Can you get two little bumpin" hats from somewhere? Then these two children can jump up for a ride on the pony next time you come by."

How could I say no?

"Tell 'ee what," Mrs Lee said when we were all standing stroking the pony's long mane. "There's a jumble sale up the village hall Saturday. You go and look. Never know what you find at them sales. There's a woman lives down the lane from here, snooty piece who don't give me the time o' day. Her young ones, what used to ride is growed up. When they come round collecting jumble I'll sent they to she." I knew what she meant and smiled to myself at her cunning.

"How do you know she won't just give a load of old clothes?"

"Cos I'll tell them what's collecting to ask for fancy stuff. To make more money. They keeps on about the sale being for a good cause so I'll tell them to ask old snooty-pants for them children's bumpin' hats and fancy riding trousers. They'll make a penny or two, more than her old knickers."

The children danced with glee as they always did when Mrs Lee's anarchic behaviour delighted them.

"Come and see me bedroom," she said with pride, "me grandson papered it for me. He do live with I not his Mother. She's all right me daughter but I don't get on wi' she, no more do he so he lives here now." She flung the door to her bedroom open and I gasped.

"Lovely en' it?"

The paper had a gothic design in deep burgundy-red flock. It made Mrs Lee's bedroom as gloomy as a funeral parlour but she was so delighted that I could only echo her words in tones so weak she took them as a sign that I was almost speechless with admiration.

We left with promises to return soon with 'bumpin' hats.

Peter came home full of tales from the surgery which he recounted when the children were in bed.

"My first patient was a retired doctor down here on holiday. He used to practice in a small country town. He told me that he never went out without a

G.Younger

piece of string in his pocket and a shilling."

I looked suitably mystified, "go on."

"The shilling was to feed the gas meter so that he would not have to examine his patient by torchlight if the meter ran out."

"And the string?"

"Ah that was for tying the umbilical cord if he arrived to an unexpected delivery." Peter sat back looking pleased with himself. "He was quite surprised when I told him that I had one of those recently. He thought concealed pregnancies had gone out with the advent of the pill."

"Just out of interest, what did you tie that umbilical cord with?"

Peter looked sheepish as he said, "I didn't. I hadn't even delivered the placenta when Nurse Jackson arrived with clamps in her bag." Peter added, "talking about concealing things I had another interesting example of that today." He cupped his hands around his coffee mug, "a lad came in with his arms covered in sticking plasters. When I asked him if he'd been in a briar patch he blushed and began to peel them off." Peter drank his coffee.

"Go on," I urged him, "what next?"

"Under the plasters were tattooed girls names and four letter words. Apparently when he got married recently he covered all the names of his past girl friends and the rude words with the plasters. Now his new wife is beginning to ask what he has done to his arms and when he's taking the plasters off!"

"But what did he want you to do about it?"

"He wants an appointment to have his tattoos removed as fast as possible. When I told him the waiting list for plastic surgery he nearly passed out. I had to tell him that his was hardly an urgent problem and if he really wants to have his past erased quickly he'll have to pay to have that done privately. The sum I mentioned nearly turned him faint again."

"Oh dear," I smiled ruefully, "he's going to have to own up to his past isn't he. Unless he can get away with never having a bath."

Peter grinned, "the plasters are dirty already and rolling at the edges. My guess is his new wife will choose her moment in bed and yank one of them off!"

"What a thought. Confronting the name of a past rival and four letter words in bed!"

When I went downstairs next morning I unlocked the front door to take in the milk when I noticed something wrapped in newspaper tucked behind the milk bottles. I carried the bottles and the parcel into the kitchen. On the kitchen table the newspaper parcel unrolled and I found a bunch of watercress, still dripping with river water. Inside, scribbled on a corner of the newspaper, was a message in pencil "Cress for a very kind doctor".

"Watercress," Peter exclaimed when he came downstairs. "Some of my older patients tell me they eat it to help their rheumatism."

"I wonder who picked this for you," I stood the bunch of cress in a jar of water.

"I don't know," Peter said, "but wash it well before you eat any of it. Watercress can carry a sheep's parasite in the hollow stems. Mind you, there aren't many sheep around here so it should be safe enough. By the way, the roof trusses are going up on the new surgery today. Do you want to bring the children down to see? Come at the end of morning surgery before Joan goes home."

By the time we went down to the surgery at half-past-ten all but the last few roof timbers were in place.

"It begins to look like a real building now, doesn't it?" I said as Peter and I stood looking at the skeleton roof being erected on the new brick walls. "Shouldn't we start thinking about some furniture?"

"Umm," Peter sighed, "I had an office furniture catalogue through the post the other day but everything in it was so expensive. I'll have to keep using Father's old desk and chair for now. We are building in a work-top for Joan to work on in the reception area but we do need chairs for the waiting room."

"What's wrong with more old chairs to go with the ones you inherited from Dr Thomas?" I asked, "we could go to some auction sales and pick up sets of dining chairs that will do until we can afford to replace them with fancy ones."

Peter looked relieved. "I'll look in the local paper and see if there are any sales coming up."

"I think I'll take those two home," I said watching Clare and James clambering over the builder's piles of sand and bricks.

The children were more than usually grumpy when I made them leave their new play-ground and come home. They dragged their feet on the way home until a sudden summer shower made us run for shelter under one of the lime trees which overhung the lane. We were not the only ones to seek the lime tree's shelter. A tall angular lady, whom I recognised as Mrs King, the eccentric lady of the manor, was also sheltering from the shower. I knew that she no longer lived in the manor but in the converted stables nearby.

"I don't believe we have been introduced," she began, eyeing my children severely from beneath the crumpled linen hat she wore low on her brow. "I am Mrs King and you are Mrs Stratford I believe?" She held out her hand, "and these are?" I introduced the children with misgivings but they were silenced by Mrs King's formal handshake. She frowned. "These children are hot," she put a bony hand on James's brow and to my surprise he did not wriggle free but stared at her in surprise. Some spirit of the Victorian nursery seemed to emanate from her. "Very hot," she looked at me, "I would say that they are sickening for something. Usual story I suppose, the cobbler's children are always worst shod. I don't expect your overworked husband ever spares his own family a professional glance."

Startled, I looked properly at the children and began to wonder.

"The minute this rain eases you must take them home," Mrs King went on in the tones of someone used to obedience. "I brought up four children myself." She sniffed delicately, rummaged in the pocket of her skirt and pulled out a huge linen square. "Humph, a table napkin not a handkerchief, look alike in the wash don't they? Oh well," she blew her nose heartily, "I do use them for handkerchiefs sometimes but never," she stared hard at the children, "at the same time you understand. Your mother will never see either of you children wiping your noses on the table napkins I trust."

I began to warm to Mrs King. She peered out from under the shelter of the tree. "This rain is passing over. Now, when these children have recovered from whatever they are incubating, come and have tea with me. My bees make very good honey from these lime trees. I will telephone you. Good morning." She marched away down the wet lane.

Rumbles of thunder followed us home. Clare looked apprehensively at the hills around the village. Bruised clouds were spreading over the valley and the sound of thunder drew nearer. We got inside the cottage just as huge drops of storm rain hit the path behind us.

"I don't like that noise," Clare whimpered.

"And I don't like these," James declared, pulling up his shirt to display a fine crop of blistery spots.

"Oh, didn't I say?" Peter replied at lunch time when I challenged him, "there's quite an epidemic of chicken pox in the village. Lucky it isn't term-time." He went upstairs to the children's room and gave their spots a cursory glance. "They'll live." He looked at his watch. "Must go, I've got a list of people to see and a consultant coming from the hospital to do a domiciliary visit this afternoon."

"I won't be able to go out," I said gloomily, facing an afternoon with two itchy and demanding children. "I might start painting the kitchen cupboard." We had been given an old kitchen cupboard with glass-fronted doors etched with crinoline ladies. I had already washed, rubbed down and undercoated the wooden parts of the cupboard which now stood, in the centre of the kitchen, awaiting its final coat of white paint. The children woke up scratching and grizzling when I was painting the fiddly bits of framing around the glass doors. I left my brushes in a jam jar of spirit and went upstairs to put James and Clare in a cool bath to ease the irritation of their spots.

"You're all spotty too," James said accusingly when he saw my paint splattered jeans." You've got white spots on your nose." I had just lifted the children out of the bath, dried them and anointed their poxy spots with calamine lotion when I heard the front door open.

"Annie," Peter's tone as he called up the stair-well made me suspicious.

"Daddy, we've got lots of spots, look," James and Clare ran downstairs, the pair of them wearing only calamine lotion. When I turned the corner of the staircase I saw a tall distinguished looking man in the hall and Peter fending off his naked pink-painted children.

"Annie, this is Dr Alexander." I could see from the look on Peter's face that he had not expected to find me splattered with paint. "We've been to visit old Mrs Richards," he smiled weakly. Dr Alexander held out an immaculate hand. "Peter said you would be kind enough to make some tea before I have to drive back to the hospital." He was the sort of consultant physician that my old ward sister had practically curtseyed to. I suddenly felt as if I had been caught with a loaded bedpan in my hand.

"Do go through into the sitting room," I flapped a paint-speckled hand, "I'll - er just put the kettle on." I gave Peter a look behind Dr Alexander's back which I hoped expressed my feelings. Peter lifted his hands helplessly.

"Bed you two," I hissed at the startled children. "Stay there until I come up." I went into the kitchen to fill the kettle and find cups for a tea tray. With a sinking heart I looked in the biscuit tin. Three stale digestive biscuits sat among the crumbs. When I took the tea tray through to the sitting room Dr Alexander smiled graciously. "Oh how kind and how welcome. I was just telling Peter what a pleasure it is to come out sometimes and see patients in their homes."

And GP's in theirs, I thought as I poured the tea.

"We do tend to be remote from reality in our hospital wards you know," he said as he accepted his cup of tea. I smiled though gritted teeth and offered three biscuits on the smallest plate I had been able to find.

"I must just … er … see if the children are all right," I retreated and left the two men to enjoy their conversation about diabetes over stale digestive biscuits. As Peter complained hours later, "they weren't even chocolate biscuits."

"Well if you had warned me that you were bringing Old Harley Street home I would have bought some." I said crossly. I had a headache and felt as if I might be getting a cold but I knew better than to say so to Peter. The next morning I hardly knew how to crawl out of bed. Peter also seemed to be out of sorts. By the time the children's spots had faded we were, as the locals say, fair diggered with chicken pox too. Dr Thomas worked while Peter was infectious. He reported that we were the joke of the week in the village. "You might have been forgiven for contracting something adult like shingles," he told Peter on the telephone, "but chicken pox is for children."

Peter recovered first and returned to work which also meant returning to night calls. I was still covered in angry spots and feeling very sorry for myself when we were woken up one night.

"OK," I heard Peter say, "I'll come right away." He got out of bed and dressed hurriedly. I groaned and pulled the sheet over my eyes when he put the light on. After I heard his car pull away I fell into a deep sleep only to be woken by the telephone ringing again. I nudged Peter but there was no one there. The space beside me was cold and empty. I peered at the bedside clock as I picked up the telephone. Peter had been out over an hour.

"Dr Stratford's house," I croaked. "An anxious man's voice told me that his wife seemed to be unwell. Resisting the temptation to say "that makes two of us," I found out that his wife was covered in spots which did seem to make two of us. I tried explaining that Peter had been called out already and that there was little he would do for chicken pox at three in the morning anyway but the patient's husband was not pleased.

"I think my wife needs to be seen by a doctor," he told me angrily. She should be so lucky I thought, but said, "well I am really sorry but he isn't here as I have explained. Give me your telephone number and I will get him to ring you when he gets back."

When Peter returned I mumbled at him from the depths of sleep to telephone the number I had scribbled down. He sat on the bed and dialled the number. It rang for a long time before it was answered.

"Dr Stratford here. I believe you rang earlier?"

I heard the man shout, "my wife was asleep until you woke her up again," he slammed the telephone down.

"Your wife was asleep too," I grumbled as Peter rolled into bed. "What have you been to?"

"Four teenagers who crashed a car returning from a birthday party." He punched his pillow. "They were all dead."

I lay awake for a long time thinking of the parents who had nursed their children through chicken pox, measles and all the other childhood ailments only to have them die in a heap of metal. My sense of proportion returned and I fell asleep. In the morning I felt well again.

The summons to Mrs King's house came at the end of the next week. "I hear that you are all out of quarantine," her voice boomed down the telephone early one afternoon. "Come to tea this afternoon."

"I will have to wait until Joan returns to answer the telephone," I explained. Mrs King seemed to accept this as a sign of proper wifely duty.

"Come to the door in the high wall, "she told me as she rang off.

The afternoon was overcast and slightly chilly as we set off for Mrs King's house. I had been indoors so much in the preceding weeks that I had not realised how far autumn had advanced. Over our heads the swallows were gathering on the telegraph wires. In the hedge half-ripe blackberries showed every colour from garnet through purple; the berries of a guelder rose set the seal on autumn.

We walked past the Manor House, which had been turned into flats for distressed gentlefolk who kept Peter very busy, towards the old stables. I knocked on the door in the high stone wall.

"Come in." Mrs King opened the door and we stepped into a conservatory which had been built on to the inside of the high wall.

"Sit down," Mrs King pointed me towards a pair of Victorian buttonback chairs. "Children, come with me," she ordered and they followed her into the kitchen I could see through a door. I sat down and breathed in the smell of scented-leaved geraniums and ferns. The flagstoned path outside was covered with apples set out to ripen.

"The children have chosen their cups," Mrs King said when she carried a battered tin tray through and put it on the bamboo table between our chairs. I was horrified to see that James appeared to have chosen a Coronation Mug with King George the Fifth's head on it while Clare was tenderly cradling a tiny cup of bone china so thin that I could see her fingers through it.

"Don't look so worried," Mrs King began to pour pale tea from a silver teapot, "children are perfectly capable of doing the right thing if it is expected of them. I continually marvel when I hear young mothers shouting at their children that they will fall, or be sick. What else do they expect of their children if they cannot trust them to behave? Clare and James are going to look for fallen apples for me when they have drunk their milk. A rock cake my dear?" Mrs King handed me a plate of rock cakes which lived up to their name but the tea was fragrant and her conversation bracing. The children drained their milk and quietly went out of the garden door. I watched as they picked up two baskets from a low flat-topped wall before opening a wicket gate and vanishing in the direction of an orchard. Mrs King's conversation was of the Women's Institute and an Embassy where she had lived when her children were small. I drank my tea in a daze. I felt the languor of convalescence and something else, as if I had strayed into another world like Alice. I watched as the children returned sedately through the wicket gate.

Mrs King called to them through the door, "remember now, keepers to ripen, bruised ones in the kitchen." James and Clare squatted down on their haunches, picked out the best apples, and placed them in the jigsaw of apples laid out on the path to ripen. They brought the rest to Mrs King for inspection.

"Take them to the kitchen. You may chose some to take home and leave the rest on the table. When James tipped four shiny green apples into my lap Mrs King said briefly, "dumpling apples. Brown sugar in the middle and pastry outside." She stood up and collected the cups onto the tray; I took the hint. She showed us back to the door to the lane.

"When you have time, go and see Emily Mundy, Woodbine Cottage. You'll like her. She's expecting to see you sometime."

I barely had time to thank her before she had closed the door in the high wall behind us and vanished like the white rabbit.

❧

Peter was on duty at a pony club event the following weekend so we all went with him. James and Clare were impressed at first by the children, no older than themselves, in jodhpurs and tailored jackets with polished boots and leather whips. We watched as they mounted barrel-shaped ponies and began relay races. The children's eyes were on the racing ponies, mine were on the well-dressed parents urging their children on. The crowd gasped with collective sympathy when a small boy fell off. Peter started forward but the child's mother got there first.

"You stupid boy," she pushed him back into the saddle. The child's face was white. I saw him look in mute appeal at his father who shouted, "get on with it, Jonathan." Father had purple-veined cheeks and piggy eyes.

After half-an-hour of watching ambitious parents urging their children on, I'd had enough.

"We'll walk home," I said to Peter.

He nodded, "you do that. I'm stuck here until they finish the last race."

"Yes, well at least you *are* here to help if one of them breaks any bones. Come on children." To my surprise they followed me without complaint.

Can we go and see Mrs Lee's pony on the way home?" James said in a subdued voice.

"What a good idea. Come on." We walked over the fields back to the village and Mrs Lee's house. She was picking plums in her garden.

"Ah now, I am glad to see you all out and about again," she exclaimed as a smile creased her brown face. "I heard about the spots. You missed the jumble sale but I got them." Triumphantly she led us to her breeze-block porch where she dragged out a cardboard box full of old clothes. "Go on then," she pushed it towards the children, "have a look in there." She winked at me as they began to rummage around as if the box were a bran tub of prizes.

"I found one, it's a bumping hat!" James crammed the riding hat on his head just as Clare found another one. I did the chin straps up safely as Mrs Lee went into the paddock to catch the pony. She lifted James up onto his uncomplaining back.

"Hold on to his mane," she told James, "he 'ent got no bridle on mind. You hang on to your brother," she said as she lifted Clare up behind James. Mrs Lee put her hand on the pony's neck and clicked her tongue until the quiet old pony began to move slowly forward. As I stood back to watch, the tune Widdicombe Fair ran through my head. I remembered the musical jug which stood for years on my grandmother's shelf, she had bought it at Widdicombe before the war. Painted on the side of the jug was the old grey mare with her burden of seven riders, Old Uncle Tom Cobley and all. If you lifted the jug and wound the key, the musical box hidden in the false bottom of the jug played the tune Widdecombe Fair over and over again. The children laughed as they rode slowly round the paddock. I wondered what the hard-faced pony club parents with the big cars and horse boxes would have made of Mrs Lee. And what their well-dressed children would have made of the pony and the children's jumble sale riding hats. I knew which children I thought were enjoying themselves the most. I sat on the wall singing softly to myself, "Old Uncle Tom Cobley and all, Old Uncle Tom Cobley and all."

# Sales & Cider

"THERE'S A FARM SALE ON Wednesday," Peter said, looking up from the local paper, "shall we go and see if we can get some chairs for the new surgery waiting room?"

On Peter's half day we drove though the lanes in search of the farm where the sale was to be held.

"I thought I had got to know this patch of country quite well," Peter muttered as we came to yet another crossroads. I looked at the white finger post. "I think we've been here before. In fact, I think we are going in circles."

"Very possibly," Peter snapped. A battered car with a small trailer behind it lurched past us, "I'm following him," Peter swung the car rapidly left and we shot out in pursuit of the car and trailer. I knew better than to comment when Peter sat hunched over the wheel with a grim expression on his face. Suddenly the car we were following turned into the hedge and disappeared.

"No wonder we've driven past before," Peter exclaimed as he drove through the overgrown entrance to a farm track. Immediately I saw a board tacked to a post driven at a drunken angle into the field edge; it read TO THE SALE with an arrow pointing down the rutted track.

"Ah, this looks more like it," Peter relaxed in his seat as we saw a long line of cars parked ahead at all angles, their nearside wheels in the ditch. Farmers and their wives, dressed in their Sunday best, stood in groups or walked towards the farmhouse visible between the trees. We parked, got out and followed. I felt underdressed in jeans. The farmers all wore suits from the 1950's. They favoured shirts with oversized collars as if they could hardly bear the constriction of a shirt and tie on their sunburned necks. Their wives were in herbaceous-border print dresses subdued by knitted cardigans.

The auctioneer had set up a table under an open-fronted barn where a young man handed out sale catalogues. Peter took one and we studied it.

"Well I don't think we really have a use for a Fordson tractor *circa* 1955," Peter read, "or any of the farm deadstock."

"That sounds grim," I said trying to read over his shoulder.

"Dead stock just means tools and so on not dead animals," Peter strode off," let's go and see what's in the house itself."

Paper arrows pinned to fences pointed us towards the back door of the farmhouse. As we ducked under the lintel we heard voices. To our left was a dark lean-to outbuilding full of men. Peter gestured to me with his head. Under our feet the floor was gritty. The cobwebs overhead were blackened with years of coal dust.

"This is like Mr Bailey's shed," I whispered to Peter, who frowned at me. He seemed to think that silent gestures or whispers were as necessary as if we were attending an auction of valuable antiques. The walls of the lean-to were lined with old tools tied together in bundles with lot numbers attached. While Peter inspected them earnestly I looked along shelves lined with rusty tins which had once held National Dried Milk and powdered egg. I wondered why dried milk and powdered egg should ever have been needed on a farm even in war-time. A low window let in greenish light. Tall nettles tapped on the dirty window-pane.

"I'm going to look in the kitchen," I whispered to Peter. He nodded knowingly. The kitchen was full of women inspecting the numbered lots of burnt and battered saucepans, piled china and bundled cutlery. They seemed uninterested in the pine table or the chairs underneath. A lone man, whom I immediately cast as a dealer, was covertly looking over a brown-painted dresser. I could imagine the dresser stripped of its paint in a showroom of pine furniture with a big price tag. The chairs were a kitchen collection of mixed styles. I took their lot number down and went through into the next room, a parlour full of mahogany where I found nothing of interest for the surgery. Upstairs the bedrooms were so quiet that I felt an intruder; high uncomfortable looking beds were piled with bundles of bed linen. Items coyly called bedroom china in the catalogue were lined up on a low chest of drawers; rose-painted china chamber pots and children's tin pots which reminded me of the childhood embarrassment of using a metal pot in the silence of the night. I wandered through to another room under the eaves where Peter found me.

"Look at all this," I showed him a bundle of linen, lot 89, huckaback towels and pillow-slips with crocheted edges, hand-embroidered dressing table sets and white crocheted bedspreads. "Women spent hours making all these, now nobody wants them," I fingered a tray-cloth of fine drawn-thread work, "it seems wrong to sell things like this, they should be heirlooms kept in the family."

"There isn't one," Peter lifted a Lloyd Loom chair to inspect it for worm, "the old man was in the cottage hospital when we arrived. I remember when he died we could not find any next of kin. Someone told me that when his sons were killed in the war his wife drowned herself in a mill pond."

"I wonder who has inherited the house?" I smoothed the edges of the linen pile back in place, "whoever it is doesn't want lot 89."

A distant bell rang, "the auction's starting." Peter ducked out of the low bedroom door and we went down the stairs comparing notes on the likely lot numbers we had found. The auctioneer was a red-faced man with a sense of humour to match. He got through the lot numbers at a fast pace and I felt Peter's tension rise when the kitchen chairs were the next lot.

"Right ladies and gentlemen, who will start me at a pound each for these sturdy chairs?"

The auctioneer's eyes went round the packed kitchen to the doorway where people were still trying to shoulder in. No one moved a muscle.

"Fifty pence then, ten shillings in old money. Come, come, chairs like these must be worth ten shillings of anyone's money."

I felt a movement and saw Peter lift one corner of his catalogue.

"Fifty pence I have, only fifty pence for each of these fine old kitchen chairs. Any more? Yes sir, one pound? One pound each I am bid. One pound fifty?"

I turned cautiously to see who was competing with us for the chairs. The dealer leaned indolently against the dresser. He had already bid for, and bought, the table for ten pounds.

"He wants the set," I whispered to Peter who ignored me and raised his catalogue again.

"Thank you Sir, one pound and fifty pence each chair, any advance on that?" The dealer shrugged and shook his head. The auctioneer raised his hammer, looked round the room, then tapped his table looking at Peter, "yours Sir for one pound fifty each."

We wriggled out of the crowd as the bidding began for the dresser. Out in the yard Peter took a deep breath, "phew, six pounds for a few old chairs."

"Yes but what price four new office chairs?" I consoled him as we walked over to the van selling tea and coffee. We took our mugs of dark tea and pieces of yellow slab cake to a line of chairs under the farmhouse veranda. From inside we could hear the bidding.

"I'm going to bid for lot 89," I said when I had finished my tea.

"What on earth do you want with all that old stuff," Peter began to object as we stood up. As I unhooked my shoulder bag from the chair back I noticed something. "Hey these chairs have got lot numbers stuck to them."

Peter turned round in surprise and looked at them. The white painted chairs were lot 90 described in the catalogue as garden chairs. We inspected them quickly.

"These chairs haven't been kept outside in the garden," Peter turned a chair upside down. "I reckon they're oak," he said with suppressed excitement, "good plain country dining chairs covered in white paint."

I left him standing near the chairs trying to look nonchalant as I ran upstairs to bid for lot 89. No one else wanted the linen bundle which was knocked down to me for fifty pence. I rushed down to the auctioneer's desk to pay and collect my receipt. On his way to start the bidding for the garden tools laid out on the lawn I heard the auctioneer pause by Peter's chairs. The dealer was across the yard buying tea at the van window. Peter bought the whole set of chairs for one pound.

"Nobody wanted them," he whispered triumphantly as he joined me in the queue to pay." Four matching oak chairs for one pound but six pounds for four odd pine chairs!"

"That's auction sales for you," I said as if I was an old hand. We grinned at each other. Then Peter pulled a face, "we should have bought both cars. How do we get them all home?"

"Excuse me butting in, doctor, but do you want me to bring one lot of them chairs for you?" A young man in shirt sleeves smiled at us as he turned away from the auctioneer's table with his receipt. "I slipped over before milking to bid for one of the old tractors but he went past my price, I've got the Land Rover," he jerked a thumb towards the line of parked vehicles, "all I've got to put in it is this clock I bought for my uncle," he showed me the receipt in his hand.

"That's very kind of you Jack," Peter introduced me to the sandy-haired farmer, "if you're sure it's no trouble ... ?"

"No trouble, I'll see you back by the Land Rover when I've got the clock." The young man loped off in the direction of the farmhouse parlour.

I took my receipt and went up the stairs to collect my bundle of linen and took it out to the car. Peter was tying the pine chairs on to the roof rack. "We'll put the oak ones in Jack's Land Rover, they're heavy."

We carried the chairs out to the parked Land Rover where Jack was about to tie a sack around the bracket clock he had bought.

"That's a fine clock," I said, admiring the painted dial.

"You should see the rest of uncle Harry's collection if you like clocks," Jack tied the sack covered clock to the back of the driver's seat. "He's got clocks everywhere."

"I'd love to see them."

"Come with me when I deliver this one, I'll drop your chairs off first."

When we got home we were just unloading the chairs from our car roof when the district nurse's Mini drove up to the cottage gate. I saw a shadow pass over Peter's face. He was off duty and in no mood to be drawn back into work. But as soon as I saw Nurse Jackson's expression I knew something serious had brought her to our door. Jack's Land Rover drew up behind her and he began to unload the second set of chairs.

"What is it?" Peter put down the two chairs he was carrying on the garden path as Nurse Jackson came towards us.

Her face was crumpled with distress. "I've just been to see old Mr Hardiman, the chap with cancer of the throat. I let myself in by the back door like I always do," she leaned against our car wearily, "he was dead in a chair in the living room." Her normally ruddy face was pale.

Peter opened the car door, "I'll come back with you. Is there a phone in his house? I'll need to get hold of the coroner's officer and an undertaker when I have certified him as dead. I suppose … ?"

"Oh no doubt about that," she sighed, "he must have been there all night."

"OK, let's go," Peter got back into the car. "I'll see you sometime, Annie."

"Wait," I reached into the car boot, removed my bundle of linen and closed the boot lid. Peter drove away leaving me and Jack standing in the lane with our piles of chairs.

Jack shook his head, "depressing things they have to see to sometimes don't they, your husband and the nurse. I'll help you get these chairs indoors. We'll leave the visit to my uncle's clocks for another day."

I hugged my bundle of linen, "I would love to see them, it will be something to look forward to. I couldn't have spent long at your uncle's this afternoon anyway, I have to collect the children soon."

"Bring them with you when you come. Uncle loves youngsters. How about Friday afternoon?"

We carried the chairs to the stone shed in the garden where they would have to stay until the surgery waiting room was painted and ready to receive them.

After Jack drove away I gathered myself together and set off down the lane to Cowslip Cottage to collect the children. I found them all in the garden, Mr and Mrs Hayward had brought out an ancient croquet set.

"Do we have to come home?" James said crossly when I appeared through the side gate.

"It's high time we got some work done anyway," Mrs Hayward said gently. "We have all the watering to do and the hens to feed. You can come and play another afternoon."

I walked back to the cottage feeling very flat. The children trailed reluctantly behind me pulling at grasses angrily. I thought about the sale in the farmhouse which had once been a family home and was now empty of its contents waiting for a buyer; and the patient dying alone while village life went on outside his door.

"We're going to pick runner beans for supper," I said as soon as we were back home. The children's mulish expressions did not change but I gave them each a basket and we went down the garden to the bean row. Clare and James crouched down to peer under the leaves for the longest beans.

"They've got fluff on them," Clare complained. She brought a stringy old bean to me. Stuck to its rough surface was a wisp of thistledown.

"It's down from the field thistles, look." I lifted her up on to the wall, James scrambled up beside her. Along the field edge, among the long bleached grasses missed by the mower were tall heads of thistledown.

"Ssh, keep still," I whispered as I saw two birds fly to the nearest clump of thistles. More members of the goldfinch family arrived chattering like canaries. Displaying their gold wing bars the birds fluttered over the thistles and clung to the downy heads . As mysteriously as they had arrived they flew away. I remembered that the collective name for a group of goldfinches is a charm and the shadow lifted.

"Any chance you would like to come and do some apple picking?" a voice said when we were carrying our baskets of beans back towards the house. Walt Ford was peering over the garden wall. "I can't get at them, can't eat them all either come to that."

I felt the shadows retreat further, "of course I'll come and pick apples Mr Ford, I'll have to bring these two with me though."

He sniffed, "well they *might* be some help I suppose. You know what they'd say though don't you? Two boys is half a boy and three boys is no boy at all."

"I'm not a boy," Clare told him indignantly.

"Well same thing," Walt sniffed, "children are all the same when it comes to work. Mind you" he winked at them, "women's the same too, never say no to a few free apples like Eve. You three come along to my old orchard sometime. Knock on the door when you come."

The next day, when news of Mr Hardiman's death was round the village, we went to Walt's orchard.

"I didn't even know you had this patch of ground Mr Ford," I said as we stood among the low trees hung with ripe apples.

Mr Ford rested his weight on the trunk of a fallen apple tree which had managed to flower and fruit, "best place in the world this is," he put both hands on his stick, "if I have to go to Moreton or, God forbid, to Bristol, I comes back here and sits on this old tree and I reckon it's like being in Heaven with the gate shut."

Fallen apples lay in the long grass, full of wasps drunk on their fermented juice, I looked around for a ladder.

"I don't use no ladder," Walt heaved himself to his feet. "Long time since I could climb a ladder. See they cider apple trees over there?" he pointed to trees hung with red and yellow apples the size of Christmas tree baubles. Canvases were spread under the trees.

"I just shake the tree and the canvas catches the fruit when they come down. I got a couple of lads what comes and shovels they up for me."

In the corner of the orchard I saw a high-sided trailer heaped with small apples.

"When I can borrow me brother's tractor I shall haul that lot to his farm, Eddie's got a press you see."

"A working cider press?" I was intrigued, "I would love to see that."

Walt shrugged, "you go along anywhen. Tell him I sent you, he won't mind."

I began to pick eating apples from low branches heavy with fruit. The basket I had left in the long grass was soon full.

"You'll want these," Walt came hobbling over with four huge green and red striped apples. "Dumplin' apples," he sniffed, "you do know how to make apple dumplins I suppose?"

I was saved from replying by the children who came running from the far side of the orchard with purple-black plums the size of duck eggs in their hands. "You can eat they," Walt told them. Turning to me he added, "you can have a bucket of plums if you want them?"

"If you can spare them?" I said as the children sank their teeth into the plums. Purple juice ran down their chins.

"Well if I eat all the plums I got in this orchard, I wont have no stoppage," Walt stumped over to a shed and returned with an enamel bucket. "Go and fill he up with plums for your mother," he gave the bucket to James, "watch out for wasps mind."

When Peter came home from surgery at lunchtime he had already visited to Eddie Ford's farm and seen the cider press.

"How about this then?" He carried a giant sized whisky bottle into the kitchen. It was filled with a cloudy looking liquid.

"That looks like the scrumpy that Alf bought to take to Bert, my first patient, when he was in hospital," I said, eyeing the bottle and remembering Mr Polkinhorne's under-the-counter supply.

"Eddie Ford filled this for me out of his own barrel." Peter sat down at the kitchen table. "I went to see him this morning because I had a message that he was ill. When I got there he was in the yard working. Said he'd had stomach pains but they'd passed off." Peter grinned, "he had the grace to apologise, it's a long way down his farm track. Then he invited me to see his cider press."

"Did you see the press working then?" I said enviously.

"I smelt it more than saw it," Peter said, "the press is in a dark old barn and I was dazzled from the sun outside but the smell - pure nectar of apples. Eddie took me into another barn where his barrels were lined up against the wall with mugs on hooks above them. The old man had a glass down before I saw his hand move," Peter grinned, "he pulled the spiggot and started filling it for me, "here you try a bit o' this Doc", he said. When I told him that I couldn't sample his cider in the middle of a working day he drained the glass himself and filled this bottle for me to bring home. Oh, and there's a pig's head and a goose's egg in the car."

I stared at him, "what am I supposed to do with a pig's head?"

"Well," Peter hesitated, "make brawn?

"Brawn! You mean that gristly cold meat that looks like pink marble and tastes disgusting! I know my cooking is more Cordon Bucolic than Cordon Bleu but I draw the line at cooking pigs' heads."

"Well what am I to do with the thing? I can't visit patients with a severed pigs head sitting on the back seat of my car."

"Bury it in the garden," I folded my arms and tried to look implacable. "I'll make an omelette with the goose egg though," I said in mollifying tones.

The egg made four huge omelettes. After lunch Peter went out to his car to deal with its grisly occupant. He came back as I was clearing the table looking pleased with himself.

"I met old Granny Watkins outside and offered her the pig's head. Pleased her more than a bouquet!"

I went to the window and glanced out to see Granny Watkins beetling up the lane cradling the pig's head like a baby wrapped in newspaper.

On a wet Saturday morning I went into the village for a loaf and saw that there was a jumble sale in the village hall. I joined the queue of umbrellas.

"Where's your brolly then?" Mrs Lee asked when we met in the queue.

"I've got a hood, it leaves my hands free," I said, indicating my shopping bag and two wandering children.

"You don't need your brolly for the rain," she said, looking at our neighbours in the queue, "you wait and see."

When the hall doors were opened the crowd surged and some of the larger ladies were almost wedged in the door as they fought to be first inside. I lost sight of Mrs Lee and hung on to the children as I was carried in on the second wave. The first wave surged against the tables piled with jumble. Garments were pulled out, measured, inspected and tossed back; the noise level rose to storm force. In the centre of the hall trestle tables piled with children's clothes could be approached from all sides so I managed to find an inlet. I was reaching for a good pair of corduroy dungarees, about Clare's size, when they were expertly hooked over my head on the end of a dripping umbrella. The two women inside the palisade of tables grimaced at me as my adversary paid for her prize. The combined smell of mothballs, wet coats and people was overpowering.

"Good morning," I half turned to see Mrs Bailey behind me. She was speaking to me – at least, her lips were moving – but I could not hear her over the roar of the crowd in the hall. She pulled at my sleeve and pointed, "over there," she mouthed. I followed her pointing finger and saw that one corner of the hall boasted a rail of clothes on hangers. I extracted myself from the press of umbrella-armed bodies. I thought I had lost the children until I saw that they were sitting with Mr Bailey at one of the card tables set up for coffee along the far side of the hall. He had treated them to glasses of orange juice. I moved over to the rail marked 'nearly new' the crowd around the hanging garments was thinner. To judge from the styles, most of the garments for sale had been new about twenty years ago but one jacket caught my attention. I reached the hangar down to inspect the coat, the label inside said Marks and Spencer size 14. The price tag was fifty pence. I felt a hum of pleasure, I had found a bargain. I tried the coat on, it was a perfect fit. In my purse I found fifty pence which I offered to the stall holder. She looked at me warily and then shook her head.

"I wouldn't, dear, if I were you," she mouthed.

"Why not?" I whispered copying her.

"Well you see, dear, the last owner … " She was interrupted by one of the sale organisers who had brought over her cup of coffee. I waited wondering if the last owner had fleas or died of an infectious disease.

She set her cup down on the window sill and returned to me.

"The last owner was your husband's receptionist. I mean it wouldn't look right would it, you the doctor's wife wearing your employees' cast-offs?" Firmly, she took the coat from my hand and hung it back on the rail before turning to pick up her coffee. Defeated, I fought my way across the room to the table where Mr and Mrs Bailey sat drinking coffee. Clare and James still had their noses in glasses of orange.

Mr Bailey unfolded one of the old and unstable village hall chairs for me. I lowered myself cautiously as one of the WI ladies brought me a cup of beige coffee.

"Not found anything?" Mrs Bailey smiled, "the hall sales take a bit of getting used to."

I watched Mrs Lee sweep past us, her arms piled with garments she had bought. She paused and flourished something from under the old clothes.

"Look at this," she waved a riding crop, "to go with the bumpin' hat." The children rose in their seats as if on horses. Mrs Lee disappeared in the crowd. I sipped my coffee which was indistinguishable from tea either by taste or smell.

"Bought any cakes have you?" Mrs Bailey pulled her basket from beneath the table. Inside were two chocolate sponges thickly decorated with butter icing.

"I didn't even know there was a cake stall," I said, looking round the hall vaguely.

"Always in front of the stage dear. But it sells out in the first five minutes. You have to be quick and be prepared to fight for what you want. One of these is for Emily Mundy. She can't get up to the hall these days, her legs are too bad."

I remembered that Mrs King had told me about Emily Mundy and said that she wanted to meet me.

"Can I deliver the cake for you? Woodbine Cottage is on my way and I've heard about Mrs Mundy." I said as I stood up gingerly.

"That would be very kind," Mrs Bailey carefully transferred one of the sponges to my shopping bag. More customers came over to the tables for their coffee so I made my way carefully out of the hall guarding the cake in my bag.

Woodbine Cottage was one of a pair of brick houses which stood out in the ranks of stone cottages. We walked up the short front path and knocked on the door which was opened by a round robin of a woman with red cheeks and a tea cosy on her head.

"Come inside," she opened the door wide, "oh I know who you are," she said brushing my introduction aside, "you're Mrs Doctor and this must be Master James and Miss Clare."

I blinked. Only in novels set in the last century had I heard anyone referring to children in such deferential terms but to Emily Mundy, who had been in service, it was a normal form of address.

"Mrs Bailey sent you this." I took out the chocolate cake and set it on her kitchen table.

"Ah what a beauty. Thank you for delivering it."

"Why have you got a tea cosy on your head?" Clare asked before I had time to stop her.

"To keep my old ears warm," Mrs Mundy chuckled as she put the cake into a battered tin with a very youthful Queen Mother and her two small daughters on the lid.

"Are you going to eat all the cake?" James said accusingly as the cake disappeared under the tin's lid.

"No dear," Mrs Mundy said, "I shall share it with my lodger, old Luke. You probably know him – he's about in the village, big nose and grey beard."

I recognised the description. "I always thought he was a tramp."

"So he was, still is sometimes in a good summer," Mrs Mundy put the tin in her pantry, "most of the time he lives in my greenhouse."

"Your greenhouse! But he'll freeze in the winter," I was horrified. We followed Mrs Mundy into her living room where she sat us down on old fireside chairs.

"It's warmer than sleeping rough out in the open," Mrs Mundy smiled with complete acceptance. "He can't bear to be inside a building you see, not since he was in the war, the Great War that is. The greenhouse, being glass, makes him feel safe like he was still outside. He can see the stars but not feel the frost and rain. Now," Mrs Mundy put her hands on her apron-covered knees, "what can I find to amuse you two?"

She went to the mahogany sideboard which dominated the tiny room. From one of its drawers she brought out some creased sepia photographs and a rusty metal object.

"What this was for then?"

While the children puzzled over the pictures and the object Mrs Mundy and I talked about the village. I noticed that outside storm clouds were gathering.

"We'd better be going soon," I pointed at the window. Mrs Mundy turned to look, "my, it is going black over Moreton way. There's a storm coming. Look at those seagulls. They fly inland at this time of year. I used to love to watch them following the plough."

The seagulls' wings reflected the last of the sun as they flew white against the storm clouds.

"It's a thing for making holes in something," James suddenly said waving the metal object.

"Quite right, Master James," Mrs Mundy took the metal object. "My father was a cheese factor – he bought up cheeses from the farms to sell. This is a cheese borer," she held it in her hand and turned her wrist, "you used it like this to take out a sample of cheese. When I was a young girl I went to a cheese school to learn how to make cheddar cheese. We packed it in wicker baskets to be taken to London on the train." She glanced out of the window. "But that story will have to keep for another day. Off you go now or you will all get very wet before you get home."

The children did not want to leave. Someone who wore a tea cosy as a hat, kept a tramp in her greenhouse and had been to a cheese school was much more interesting than home. However, Mrs Mundy had worked with plenty of nursery staff, she knew how to handle rebellious children. Without so much as a chocolate button to bribe them with she had us out on the front path without fuss in seconds. I was filled with admiration for her generation's disciplinary skills.

"Come and see me again," she called as we walked down her path."

We hurried down the village street under the gathering clouds. Clare tugged my hand as we passed one of the stone cottages, "what's that man doing to the house?"

I glanced at the cottage and stopped, appalled to see a man wielding a lump hammer to knock pieces off a seventeenth century stone porch.

"Whatever are you doing?" I called from the gate. The builder looked at me in surprise, "building a new porch. What's it to you?"

"But that's a seventeenth century one you're breaking up," I shouted, my anger lending me courage, I loved the village stone door covers with their curled and carved brackets.

"I've been told to build a proper enclosed porch," the builder said sullenly, "to keep the weather out," he looked with contempt at the flat-topped stone cover which merely jutted over the doorstep, "no use against the weather these old things," to make his point he swung his hammer and another piece of the stone fell to the ground. At the same time thunder began to roll around the hills and huge drops of rain splashed on the shattered stones on the path. I grabbed the children's hands and we ran home. We were wet and breathless by the time I unlocked the cottage but I left the children to undo their own wet coats. I picked up the telephone and dialled the number of a friend on the local council. I had a dispiriting conversation with him which ended with , "if the cottage is not listed there is nothing to be done."

When Peter returned from doing Saturday surgery he got the full force of my indignation.

"Seventeenth century stonework and he was just smashing it up. And I bet the same stupid council people could insist that Luke was moved out of Mrs Mundy's greenhouse and put into an old people's home to die no matter how hard we all protested."

"Hang on," Peter looked totally lost, "If you mean old Luke the tramp – what has he got to do with planning laws?"

"Well it's all the same," I claimed wildly, "bureaucrats who make rules where there shouldn't be rules and no rules where they're needed."

Peter shook his head wearily, "I'm too tired to unravel that just now. But if the old stone porch has gone it's too late to make a fuss and if the authorities start making waves about Luke I won't let them drag him away to the workhouse!" Now how about a cup of coffee?"

As I turned away to fill the kettle I realised that Peter had got power to get things done whereas I had not. Lightning silhouetted the village; church tower, trees and chimneys outlined against storm clouds.

# *Launching the New Surgery*

BY THE TIME I FOUND the opportunity to visit Jack's Uncle Harry, to see his clock collection, autumn had arrived. Every morning when I opened the curtains, mist marked the course of the stream across the field. Sometimes the mists spread over the field so that the cows, soon to be taken in for the winter, stood up to their knees in milk. Many of the birds had migrated. Movement was withdrawing from the landscape to be replaced by evidence of secret activity. On some mornings the field was white not with mist but with floss spun by numberless spiders, their gossamer sheets defined by the dew. When I collected the children from school on the afternoon of our visit to Harry's James was full of new knowledge about spiders.

"We did spiders today at school," he told me as we walked from the school gate. "The spiders webs in our field could have flown hundreds of miles."

His sister looked at him sceptically. "Spiders can't fly. Can they? she added hesitantly looking nervously up the village street for a flying corps of spiders.

"No, silly," James was developing a masculine tone of scorn. "Spiders spin webs on warm mornings and they float up when the air rises," James was clearly quoting his teacher but Clare looked impressed. "Then it gets cold at night and the webs float down miles away."

"I wonder where our field gossamer was spun? " I mused as we walked down the lane that led to Harry's house. Like the gossamer, Harry's house turned out to be the stuff dreams are made of.

"How much further?" Clare began to complain as the lane plunged down between hedges of overhanging hawthorn and elder. The road was splashed with purple where birds had been gorging on elderberries in the hedge. Low afternoon light from the sky was concentrated in clusters of guelder rose berries and the sealing-wax-red hips of the wild rose.

"There it is," James suddenly pointed to chimneys and a roof ridge-line almost hidden in a tree-filled hollow.

The lane turned into a yard in front of Harry's house, long, low and built of golden Ham Hill stone the mill house had mullion windows and a stone-tiled roof.

"I can hear something," James broke away from my hand and ran to an arched grating at one end of the house.

"Come and listen," he beckoned. We joined him to hear the roar of the unseen millstream. James lay full length to peer through the grating.

A quiet country voice made us all turn round. "Good afternoon. I am very pleased to meet you. Come inside and take a cup of tea." Seeing the disappointment on the children's faces he added, "I'll take you down to see the water in the cave later if your mother says I may."

Harry's courtesy belonged to another generation. Once inside his front door we were out of time. The dark hall was lined with long-case clocks standing shoulder to shoulder around the walls.

"You shall see them all," he said gently, shepherding us towards his sitting room. "Do sit down, Mrs Stratford. I will make the tea." He turned to leave the room, then stopped, "oh do you mind the cat?" He indicated a huge tabby curled up on a button-backed chair. "She wont hurt you," he told the children, "she's a lap cat. If you don't want her just put her down on the hearth-rug."

A pegged rug lay in front of the fireplace cluttered with trivets, pokers, pans, tongs and brushes behind a brass fender which reflected the flames of the log fire.

When Harry left the room I heard distant sounds of a kettle being put on a stove and the rattle of teacups. The children looked round the room – their eyes wide, their tongues for once still. I followed Clare's eyes to the ceiling where a single bulb hung between a circlet of glass crystals casting rainbows on the ceiling. The cat rose lazily, leapt from her chair to my lap and settled down. James began to roam around the room. I resisted the temptation to say "don't touch anything". He was all eyes. There were cuckoo clocks on the walls, bracket clocks on shelves and clocks under glass domes on pie-crust tables.

"Look at this Mum," he stared through a glass dome at an Arcadian scene; a nymph modelled in gold sat on a rock bending over to catch a stream of water in an urn. The water was a spiral of glass tuned by the clock mechanism. Clare pointed silently at another dome under which a golden cherub sat on a garlanded swing which moved in time with the clock's tick.

"Here we are," Harry brought in a butler's tray almost to big to be brought through the doorway. On it were four cups shallow as porcelain dishes. I held my breath but the children, overcome by the occasion, handled their cooling cups of tea as gently as dowagers.

"Now then, I expect you would like to see more of my clocks," Harry said when we had ceremoniously drunk his tea. I stood up carefully and the cat moved to the warm nest I had left in the feather cushions. We followed Harry back though the hall.

"Now this is the Adam and Eve clock," he stood by a long-case clock where, in a painted Garden of Eden complete with lion, a goat, sheep and cows, a painted apple bounced between painted figures to the clock's tick. "This is my dragon clock," Harry said proudly moving to the next. I lifted Clare up to see the face of the black-lacquered clock where enamelled insects clicked past an open-mouthed dragon.

"Does he ever catch one?" she asked cautiously.

"I've never seen that happen," Harry answered with perfect seriousness. "Come into the dining room," he opened the door into a room almost filled by a circular mahogany table. On the marble mantelpiece was a square black clock. Above the clock face were two small doors decorated with painted flags. Harry took a key from behind the clock and began to wind it up, "this is the only one of my clocks I don't keep running and you will soon hear why." As he moved the hands of the clock to five a mechanism began to whirr. The doors flew open and the figure of a wooden bugler boy shot out like a cuckoo from a cuckoo clock, raised his bugle to his lips, and sounded a horn. Harry chuckled with pleasure at the astonishment on the children's faces. "This was a regimental clock. Whereas that one," he pointed to a big clock face balanced on a corner shelf. "That was a station wall clock, it has two faces, one for the platform and one for the waiting room."

"Why do you have so many clocks?" I asked as we followed Harry through the old dairy, lined with oak-cased clocks, towards the kitchen.

"When the mill was working this house was never silent," he opened a door for us to step into his kitchen. "The house was like a ship at sea, full of the sounds of creaking timber and moving water. I missed those sounds when I stopped milling so I started to collect clocks. They keep me company."

"Were you in the navy Harry?" I asked as we entered a kitchen warmed by a Rayburn and the smell of past meals.

He smiled, "I never saw the sea 'til I was thirty. I was born in Dorset on the estate where I worked in the livery stable. When I was sixteen all the men went off to war and I was made up to coachman in a uniform too big for me." Harry closed the dairy door to keep the draught out. "Sundays it was my job to lead the pony to pull his Lordship's Bath chair to church. I stayed outside of course." Harry smiled gently, "the pony was my job, his Lordship did the praying. In December," he went on, "I took the horses and the carriage on the train to London for her ladyship to do her Christmas shopping. I drove her to the shops, waited while she chose the presents, then drove her back to the London house. While she had her tea I drove back to each shop to collect her purchases. The shopkeepers brought them out to the carriage all properly wrapped."

"What did you make of London Harry?"

Harry stared out of the window into his dark garden as he tried to remember. "Her ladyship gave me a shilling to spend one evening. I spent it going to a picture house but there was a Zeppelin raid and we all had to leave before the film came on. I was glad to get back to Dorset."

"But you didn't stay in Dorset?"

"His lordship died not long after all his sons were killed in the war. Her ladyship put the carriage away and I had to find a new job. I came here to work and became the tenant in time."

I looked at Harry's broad back as he showed the children his kitchen long-case clock where a ship in full sail rose and dipped on a painted Bridgwater Bay. I tried to imagine him at sixteen at work in his over-large coachman's uniform not ten miles from Dorchester where Thomas Hardy was then still writing. For a moment our real world faded beside his world of horses, carriages and clocks.

"Can we see the water please?" James whispered.

Harry nodded and opened a door under the back stairs. A gust of cold mossy-smelling air made us shiver with anticipation.

"Good job I put the electric light down here," Harry said as we followed him down stone steps into a place half cellar and half cave. The single light bulb left dark corners where we could only hear the water; there was no mill wheel to see.

"The wheel went for scrap in the last war," Harry said, his voice resonant with regret. "Then I took to farming. Nowadays I've just got the one cow and my lap cat. Come on young lady," he took Clare's hand, "that water is deep and you are getting cold down here, I daresay your mother is too."

When we left Harry's house a November mist was rising from the mill stream. By the time we reached the main road the mill was wrapped in thick fog. Harry and his clocks seemed to exist in another time so when I looked back I was hardly surprised to see that the mill had vanished from sight.

A few days after our visit to the mill it was the weekend of Harvest Festival. I had been persuaded to help decorate the church. I went at the appointed time with a basket of hedge plants and garden produce. When I walked up the church path I saw neat rows of tasselled maize plants, gladioli and golden rod laid outside the vestry door, between the gravestones.

"My husband brought them over with the tractor and trailer," Mrs Bailey said emerging from the vestry door to collect an armful of maize. "We always used to give a corn stook for Harvest Festival but no one grows corn round here now, it's all fodder maize, still," she looked up at the dry stalks and tassels, "this is our modern harvest."

The vicar's wife, Mrs Straker, came out to pick up an armful of gladioli. "Ah hello, Mrs Stratford, do come in, all hands on deck you know." She carried the furled flags of gladioli into the church.

Mrs Bailey smiled at me, "she was in the Wrens during the war you know."

"I didn't know but I should have guessed," I whispered following her through the vestry into the church which smelled of apples.

The vicar's wife ran the church decorating like a naval exercise. She called out orders from beside the altar where she was filling a pedestal with stiff flowers.

"South aisle windowsill for you, Mrs Stratford," she shouted, "hop up on a pew."

I saw a few smiles from the other flower arrangers and wondered if they were aimed at the vicar's wife or the lowly status of my allotted space. I clambered on a pew, fighting a strong temptation to whistle the sailor's hornpipe as I did so, but only the vicar's wife was allowed to disturb the reverential air as women stuck chrysanthemums and Michaelmas daisies into blocks of soggy Oasis.

On the south aisle windowsill was a fallen corbel, the stone head of a lady detached in some past church restoration, propped in a window corner and forgotten. I reached over to lift the head to the centre of the windowsill. With the hankie from the pocket of my jeans I dusted the cobwebs from the folds of the stone lady's wimple. When I had used the contents of my basket to make my arrangement, her tranquil stone eyes stared out from trails of bryony and travellers' joy. I placed polished apples on the ledge beside her and then jumped down from the pew.

"Very artistic dear," Mrs Straker had marched down to the nave to check

G. Younger

on my efforts. In her clipped tones the word artistic was staccato. I was not worried, I had rather fallen for my stone lady and I thought she looked quite happy with her scarf of traveller's joy and bryony.

"Umm," the vicar's wife moved to look from another angle, "that stone head could be used as an accessory in an arrangement for a competition entitled Past and Present or something like that. Wouldn't she make a contrast to one of your lovely oriental arrangements, Mrs Avery." She appealed to a lady with blue hair, who was responsible for the arrangement of bulrushes and dead leaves behind the font.

I gathered up the twiggy bits I had dropped on the pew. "If you will excuse me I must go home now to take over the telephone." My telephone duty allowed me to leave the ladies to their floral art while I escaped into the sunshine.

On Sunday morning Peter was off duty so we joined the rest of the congregation to plough the fields and scatter noisily. After the service, coffee was served in church. As the vicar's wife handed a cup of pale coffee to Peter she said heartily, "if my husband uses that harvest sermon again next year I shall hit him with a marrow. I have heard it at every harvest service for the last twenty years! Nice little arrangement your wife has done for us doctor," she boomed as if Peter was deaf. He looked bewildered. I saw that the children were helping themselves freely from the plate of custard cream biscuits so I steered him towards the trestle table.

"Hold this," I hissed, giving him my coffee as I pushed the biscuit plate out of the children's reach. They glared at me and gulped the luminous orange juice they had been given.

"Since when have you been keen on flower arranging?" Peter murmured as he sipped his cold coffee.

"I'm not. That was my first and probably my last effort," I looked over to the windowsill where my stone lady stared sightlessly over our heads. "I bet she's seen it all," I whispered, "six centuries of village life."

"Well I won't survive another day of it if I don't get something more than cold coffee and a custard cream," Peter put his empty cup down on top of the font. "Come on you two," he hauled James and Clare out from a game of hide and seek under the choir stalls. We made our excuses and went out into the village street.

"That was boring," James said as we walked home. "I'm not going to be a vicar – I'm going to be a farmer."

"Not a doctor like Daddy," I was foolish enough to say. James stopped.

"Never," he said decisively.

We walked on in surprised silence. We approached the front door of the cottage where I saw that there was a box on the doorstep. James and Clare ran ahead to look at it.

"Leave," Peter shouted as their fingers began to prise the cardboard lid.

"Peter, they're not a pair of Labradors," I complained as we joined the children on the doorstep.

Peter picked up the box, unlocked the door and carried it into the kitchen. On the table we examined the contents of the box.

"It's a dead bird," Clare shuddered.

"Not any old dead bird," Peter said, "it's a duck and look," he moved the plucked bird and from the box pulled out a large onion, a striped cooking apple and a bunch of sage.

"Sage and onion stuffing, apple sauce and roast duck," he said in greedy tones. He looked at me, "I don't know what you had planned for our Sunday lunch but forget it, this is what we are having now."

"But this bird will take ages to cook," I protested, "and I have bought a chicken for Sunday lunch."

Peter reached into the fridge and pulled out the plate on which rested my chicken. Tenderly he removed the duck from the shoe box. There was no competition. My unfrozen supermarket offering looked soggy, pale and shrunken whereas the duck was richly coloured and plump.

"All right," I took my coat off and reached for the apron which hung on the back of the door, "you'll have to wait a long time for it."

"I'll wait," Peter opened the knife drawer, "I will even peel the apple and make the sauce and stuffing. Do you want veggies done?"

"I've already done the vegetables," I had to admit as I got down on my knees to look in a cupboard for the turkey roasting tin when a thought struck me. "Who sent this anyway, isn't there a note or anything?"

Peter pulled the newspaper packing out of the box and found a crumpled note underneath. He handed it to me as I stood up. The note, written in shaky capitals, read, "Your Michaelmas dinner," it was signed Mrs Lee. We looked at each other.

"Makes up for a few weekends on call, something like this, doesn't it," Peter said as he picked up the huge onion and began to pull of layers of skin. I took it from him, "yes it does, but go and change before you get covered in onion juice. If you ruin your jacket you'll have to go back to wearing your hairy suit," I called after him as he went to change.

At the beginning of November Dr Thomas went away to visit his married daughter so there was no one to do any locums for Peter. After two weeks without off-duty we both began to feel the strain and even the children were complaining that we couldn't take them anywhere.

"There's a village bonfire in the vicarage garden on November 5th," I told Peter one afternoon, "I know we are on duty but can we organise to get there somehow?"

"I'll see if the vicar's wife can put her telephone out on a windowsill where I can hear it," Peter said, "I've got to go and see the vicar anyway about the village charity fund. I've got a patient who needs a room heater she can't afford to buy."

Like most villages, ours has ancient charities with money which can be used for modern needs. When he came back from the vicarage Peter said, "I've sorted out the telephone for tonight. The vicar has a garden telephone bell so that he doesn't miss parish calls when he's at the bottom of the shrubbery, so that's OK."

We set off for the bonfire after dark. In the High Street we met groups of friends fat with layers of extra clothes. We all entered by the side door in the high vicarage wall. Darkness hid the weeds in the acre of ground which the vicar struggled to control. A line of jam-jar lanterns with candles inside lit the path. The effect was magical. James and Clare pulled free from our hands and rushed to join the excited children around the roped-off fire, already licking the dark sky. The church tower stood silhouetted behind the pagan scene. We gave our box of fireworks to one of the Scouts running the firework display and the hot dog stall.

"They're starting," Clare clutched my arm as the first fountain of coloured stars shot up from the grass when the church clock struck seven. Smoke from fireworks mingled with the smell of sausages and onions; firelight was reflected in laughing faces and for a short time all the pains and problems which bring people to the surgery were forgotten. Everyone looked up to watch rockets break into stars over the village chimneys.

"There's going to be a frost tonight I think," I recognised Mr Hayward's voice in the dark and then saw his face reflected in the light from the next rocket. "Well, it is winter now." He moved away into the darkness just as Peter and James returned with four hot dogs. We warmed our hands around them and licked strands of fried onions from our fingers. Suddenly a bell pealed.

"Oh damn," Peter mumbled through a mouthful of hot dog, "that's the vicar's telephone. I bet it's for me."

The children and I had eaten our hot dogs and were waiting to be given lighted sparklers when Peter returned in the smoky darkness.

"I've got to go," he whispered to me, "can you listen out for the phone and if I'm not back by the time you leave, ask the vicar's wife to answer the calls until you get back to the cottage?"

"What are you going out to?" I asked as I took the mittens thrust at me by both children when they each received a sparkler from the distributors.

Peter moved closer to whisper in my ear, "A patient in labour, no phone number I'm afraid. If you need me try ambulance control."

He vanished down the vicarage garden path. James and Clare were too intent on making patterns in the air with their sparklers to see him go. The whole garden was full of patterns of light made by invisible hands. The patterns imprinted themselves on my eyes until I was dazzled and I wondered whose baby was going to have a bonfire night birthday. When the fireworks finished and the bonfire was burning low I told the children it was time to go.

"Why must we?" Clare groaned as we turned our backs to the dying fire and walked back along the path. The candles in jam jars had burned out. Everyone used torches to find their way along the path calling in the darkness:

"Goodnight Vicar, and thank you ... Another lovely one wasn't it ... Goodnight, goodnight."

The crowd squeezed through the gate and out into the village street to walk to their warm homes through the frosty night.

"Where did Daddy go?" James said as we walked along.

"He's gone to see a patient. Come on, let's run to keep warm and get home fast or the vicar's wife will have to answer the telephone." I took their hands and we jog trotted along the lane. As we passed the turning to Bramble Lane we saw the ghostly flashing of a blue ambulance light.

"That's where Daddy is," James said with a touch of pride. The front door of a cottage stood open to the cold night. Peter's car was parked at the gate. The ambulance doors were being closed as we passed.

I had got the children to sleep before Peter came home.

"We saw the ambulance, you had time to admit her to the maternity unit then?"

Peter smiled, "yes, this wasn't going to be a rush job. The patient was still making jokes between contractions. She told the ambulance men she might call the baby Guy if it is a boy."

"I hope she doesn't," I yawned, "Poor Guy Fawkes came to a bad end didn't he?"

"Umm," Peter was falling asleep as he relaxed in his chair. He had been snoring gently for ten minutes when the telephone rang.

I could hear the excited voice from my side of the fireplace.

"It's a girl, doctor, a whopper, eight pounds."

"Ask him what the baby is to be called?" I mouthed at Peter. He frowned at me but I need not have asked, the excited voice went on, "we're calling her Stella. My wife thought of it when she saw a rocket showering stars over the garden from our neighbour's bonfire as the ambulance doors closed."

"Lovely," Peter said drowsily, "glad to hear that Mother and baby are OK, goodnight."

We went to bed and Peter fell instantly asleep. I heard the church clock strike eleven as I began to drift into dreams lit by rocket stars and flashing blue lights.

The builders finished the surgery at the end of the month; then we had painters, plumbers, electricians and carpet layers in to prepare for the day when the surgery would be open for business.

"I shall be glad to get into a warm building before the winter really starts," Peter said as we were sending out invitations to the surgery opening party. "That old caravan of Mrs Lee's is not warm. It's no wonder the old girl is so tough if she spent a lifetime of winters in that flimsy van."

"Has she found a home for it yet?" I licked another envelope.

"No. Sam is going to tow the van off the surgery site on the morning of the party and his grandmother insists he parks it back by her bungalow until she can find another use for it. I wouldn't be surprised if she doesn't go back to sleeping in it in the summer months."

"Soon we open up for business in our brand new surgery, I can hardly believe it." I stacked the invitations up into a pile. "When the winter is over we will have been here a whole year."

The days before the opening party were filled with frenetic activity as everyone from the district nurses to Mr Finch the sexton lent a hand moving the patient's notes and Peter's equipment from the caravan to the new building. I was busy cooking. Since the opening party was only a week before Christmas

I made it easy for myself by providing mince pies and mulled wine although after I had made and frozen mince pies for fifty people I wasn't sure if they were an easy option.

❧

"I'm hiding from my accountant, Anne," Dr Thomas said when I offered him another mince pie from the tray I was carrying around the surgery during the party. He had found himself a corner of the nurses room where he could enjoy his mulled wine in peace screened from the other guests by the folds of the curtain around an examination couch.

"I wish I could join you." I rested my weight on the edge of the patient's couch for a moment. "I don't know who half these people are but they're getting through my mince pies as if they travelled across the desert to get here."

Dr Thomas smiled. "Most of them have come all of three miles. Here under your new roof you have the flower of Moreton's builders and architects, bank managers and accountants with their wives." He looked at me over his gold-rimmed half-glasses. "You and I know that the guest of honour is Mrs Lee of course. Where is she by the way. If I am forced to be sociable I would be very happy to talk to one of my favourite old patients."

"She's holding court in the waiting room," I told him with a grin, "last time I passed with the mince pies she was telling the health visitor how to treat nappy rash with a herbal ointment."

"Oh I can't miss entertainment like that," Dr Thomas followed me out of the nurse's room, "I could even risk meeting my accountant on that score." We pushed our way through the crowds who were looking into all the new rooms.

"The smell of this wonderful mulled wine is disguising any antiseptic smells, Mrs Stratford," a passing man said raising his glass to me. I recognised him as one of the planning committee with whom Peter had done battle to get permission to build the surgery. "Tell me, what is this room?" he gestured with his glass into the examination room.

"This is where my husband will do minor surgery, lumps and cysts that sort of thing" I said, wickedly anticipating his swift step backwards, "another mince pie?"

He blenched, "no, er, thank you." He drained his glass and hurried away down the short corridor to the staff kitchen where my preserving pan-full of wine was simmering.

Dr Thomas gave me a wry smile, "I see that Peter is well provided with what every country doctor needs, a sensible wife."

He pinched another mince pie from my tray and disappeared into the waiting room to find Mrs Lee. I stood for a moment bemused by the waves of noise and fumes from fifty wine-laden voices. All around me well dressed people stood, glasses in hand, opening and closing their mouths.

"It's going well isn't it, you OK?" Peter had come up behind me to take another mince pie.

"That's the last one," I knew I should have made more," I whispered.

"Don't worry, they're all full of mulled wine," Peter looked around at the newly painted walls and the doors which bore signs saying Waiting Room, Office, Examination Room and Doctor's Room. "I can't really believe I won't wake up on Monday and find that I'm doing surgery in the old van."

"On Monday morning you will be sitting in state in your own consulting room," I said, looking over his shoulder to where our bank manager and his wife were looking at Peter's medical textbooks in the consulting room. "Looks as if you'd better go and talk to those two." I tried to give him a gentle push.

"Not likely, they look as if they want a quick consultation; I'll leave them with the books." Peter ducked away in the direction of the staff kitchen.

"I hear you might be interested in coming on the parish council, Mrs Stratford."

I turned to find myself cornered by the parish council chairman Mrs Avery.

"I have thought about it," I said warily, "but it's difficult for me to get to meetings with Peter's on-call duties."

"We are always looking for new blood." Mrs Avery attempted a smile.

I thought her choice of words might be very apt. I had been warned about parish politics.

"Can I get you some more orange juice Mrs Avery?" I seized her empty glass; Mrs Avery was fiercely teetotal. I made my escape into the crowd where I was waylaid by the vicar's wife.

"Good show this, Anne, got any more of the grog?"

"Follow me," I said over my shoulder as I dived into the staff kitchen, "help yourself," I filled Mrs Avery's glass with orange juice.

"Let me guess who's on that stuff," the vicar's wife said as she filled her glass with the dregs of the mulled wine, "she who signed the pledge in her cradle."

"Peter," I called as I saw him pass the door. I reached out to push the glass of orange into his hand. "Mrs Avery wants this refill. She also wants to get me on the council," I whispered, "so you take it to her."

Peter frowned, "I thought you were interested in the council, wanted to preserve all the cottages from dastardly builders and so on?"

"I do," I hissed back, "but at the moment I'm trying to preserve myself."

When our guests had all gone home we were left to survey a draining board full of dirty glasses and new carpets covered in pastry crumbs.

Peter rolled his sleeves up and filled the electric kettle. "Which do you fancy, washing up or vacuuming?"

"Neither," I groaned, " But you can't open the doors to patients on Monday morning with the place looking like a bar after a Christmas party so I'll get the vacuum cleaner out."

Peter picked up a tray and began to collect glasses from the waiting room. I dragged the vacuum cleaner from its cupboard.

"I've just remembered something you haven't done," I left the cleaner in the corridor and went to Peter's room where I opened the drawer of his desk and took out the sign which had hung on the door of Mrs Lee's caravan bedroom door. It read 'Dr Peter Stratford, MB BS.' "Go on," I gave it to him, "put it on the door then you will really have christened your new surgery."

Peter took the sign from me and hung it on the door of his consulting room. We were admiring it when the telephone started to ring on the reception desk. As Peter went to answer it I began to vacuum the waiting room carpet. He came and tapped me on the shoulder, "sorry, love, I've got to go. Sister at the Cottage Hospital needs me in Casualty." He picked up his case and made for the door. "You'll have to turn the cleaner off until I come back or you might not hear the 'phone," he said over his shoulder. The door slammed behind him and I watched through the glass door as he reversed his car and drove out of the new surgery car park. I looked down at the abandoned vacuum cleaner and thought of the piles of washing up.

"Who'd be a doctor's wife?" I muttered as I rolled up the sleeves of my best dress and walked into the staff kitchen. A sharp tap on the glass door stopped me. I went back into the corridor to see Joan peering through the glass door.

"I took Mrs Lee home," she explained, " I was coming back to help clear up when I saw doctor driving off in a hurry. Where's he gone?"

"Casualty," I sighed and started to fill the washing up bowl with hot water.

We had just finished washing up all the plates and glasses when Peter came back.

"Just in time to do the vacuuming" I said as Joan and I stacked the dry plates in a box to be taken home. "What did you have to see in casualty, nothing too drastic by your expression?"

Peter was smiling to himself as he took off his jacket. "One of our elderly patients driving slowly home from an old folks Christmas party in Moreton had a brush with a fast car."

"What's amusing you then?"

"He wasn't hurt, only a bit bruised. What tickled us all in Casualty were his comments about the dangers of all the 'erotic drivers' on the road today! If ever there was an erratic driver loose on the road it's him!"

# Christmas in Practice

THE DAYS BEFORE CHRISTMAS WERE extra busy at the surgery.

"People are coming in for their medications as if we were going to be closed for weeks!" Peter complained after a busy morning surgery. "The queue at the reception desk last night was as bad as a check-out in the supermarket."

"Don't remind me," I groaned. A bruising shopping session loomed. "We all lay in stock for a siege, it's catching. I find myself thinking perhaps we should have some of this or need more of that when I've already got enough Christmas food for an army. It's a sort of mass panic which infects us all. Mind you, I can understand people being worried that they might run out of their tablets."

"But we are open on Christmas Eve and the day after Boxing day. That's only two days without surgeries," Peter glared at the children who were arguing about the nativity play which was to take place at three o'clock.

"I'm a King so there," James put his tongue out at Clare who did the same.

"Well I'm the most important person in the whole play," she boasted, "I'm Mary."

James threw a toast crust at her." That shows how much you know. Jesus is the most important person."

"James! Behave yourself. Pick that crust up." Peter shouted.

"There has to be a Mary to have a Jesus, doesn't there Mummy?" Clare appealed to me. I could see that Peter was about to explode. The telephone rang and Peter jumped up from the table swearing under his breath.

"Be quiet you two," I whispered fiercely as I heard Peter repeating what sounded like directions to an urgent call.

"Yes, I know the farm," he was saying, "but where will I find him? Dial 999 then send somebody down to the nearest gate by the road to direct me and the ambulance men to the right place."

Peter rushed into the kitchen and pulled his coat from his chair. "This sounds like a nasty farm accident. If you need me I'm somewhere up at Green Farm. Let Joan know I'll be late will you?"

"Don't forget that I have to go to the Nativity Play in the school hall at three o'clock," I called after him, "you did remember to ask Joan to come in early this afternoon didn't you?" But Peter was already in the car and reversing out of the drive at speed when I reached the door. Back in the kitchen two subdued children appealed to me, "if you have to stay home for the phone, you wont see us in the play," James muttered.

"Don't worry, I'll find out if Joan is coming to take my place and if not," I thought quickly, "we'll use the machine."

The answering machine we had inherited from Dr Thomas was large and unreliable. It couldn't record messages but had a tape which gave a message to the caller.

"Go and get your costumes from upstairs," I told the children, "I'll see what I can do. But don't be long," I looked at my watch; it was already half past eight. I pressed the telephone intercom button which connected me to the surgery. Joan answered.

"Joan, doctor has been called to Green Farm, some sort of accident, he said to tell you that he might be delayed."

"Oh dear," Joan sounded harassed," I've already got a full waiting room. This week is always dreadful. Someone was even complaining this morning that the waiting room chairs don't match. I told him in no uncertain terms that you and the doctor had to go round the auction sales to buy them, the NHS didn't provide them!"

"Thanks for your support Joan," I hesitated to add to her problems. "Did Peter ask you to come in early this afternoon?"

"No," she answered sharply, "I've made arrangements to do some last minute Christmas shopping. A friend is driving me to Moreton." I remembered that Joan didn't drive.

"What was it for?"

"It's the children's Nativity Play at the school this afternoon. I promised them I would go, they are both in it. Is there anybody else you know of who's capable of looking after the emergency calls for an hour?"

"Mrs Ashton used to help Dr Thomas out sometimes but I know she's not well at the moment," Joan began to sound increasingly harassed, "look, I must go Mrs Stratford, I've got a queue here at the reception desk. I'll tell you what, try old Mr Beech, he lives next door to the school, if you put his telephone number on the answering machine I'm sure he would come and get you out of the school hall if necessary. He's a bit," she lowered her voice, "well - eccentric but he could manage to do that. He lives in Sorrel Cottage next to the school playground. Must go." She rang off.

"Hurry up you two," I shouted upstairs. "we've got to go *now*." James stood at the top of the stairs with his royal purple robes bundled like old washing in his arms.

"I can't find my crown," he wailed.

"I cant find Jesus," Clare shouted from their bedroom. My thoughts were completely irreligious as I ran upstairs to the room they still shared. Both bunks and most of the floor were strewn with clothes, toys and Christmas decorations.

"Well where did you put it?" I flung toys in all directions as I hunted for the plastic doll. "Don't start to cry," I yelled at Clare and cursed myself for not being the sort of organised mother who had packed everything the night before.

"If you're looking for her doll," James said scornfully from the doorway, "it's under the bath. Where's my crown?"

In the bathroom I reached under the enamel bath which Peter never had found time to box in. My fingers found a variety of abandoned plastic bath toys, an old flannel and, wedged under a bath foot, the doll.

"Ugh she's covered in spiders webs and fluff," Clare complained as I used the old flannel to wipe the doll clean.

"Never mind that no one will see once she's wrapped up to look like Jesus. I thrust the doll at her with a passing thought that Clare would probably suffer from gender confusion for ever more.

"I've remembered," James said from the bathroom doorway, "Mrs Vincent took our crowns away to stick the jewels on."

I closed my eyes for a moment, took a deep breath and said, "get in the car. There isn't time to walk to school now."

We arrived outside the school at one minute to nine. There was nowhere to park, the school bus and a milk tanker were blocking School Lane. I stopped behind the tanker, leapt out and opened the car's rear door, "out, quickly," I ordered the children. "I'll see you this afternoon. Don't worry I'll be in the hall," I called after them as they ran towards the school gate, James trailing purple garments and Clare clutching her grubby, unholy plastic doll. I reversed down the lane, left the bus and tanker to sort themselves out parked by the church and sat for a moment to draw breath. Two men were unloading a tall Christmas tree from the back of a farm trailer. I watched them manoeuvre it through the church door. As I got out of my car Mr Finch came round the corner.

"Morning, Mrs Stratford, I won't ask how you are, all you women give a sharp answer to that question just now." He nodded his head in the direction of the church door, "time to get another tree up," he sniffed, "no sooner get one Christmas over than it's time for another."

"Don't you like Christmas," I was surprised at our normally cheerful sexton's tone. He shrugged, "well it was fun when we were kids but it's all money these days I reckon." He strode off in the direction of the church and I walked along School Lane pondering on the effects of the modern Christmas. The school play-ground was empty when I walked past the railings. From the school's high gothic windows I could hear children's voices practising 'Away In A Manger' for the Nativity Play.

The cottage at the end of the school railings was the first in a rank of grey stone houses which faced the churchyard. I pushed open the gate on which was painted the name Sorrel Cottage. Two steps took me to the front door. Mr Beech opened his door. He knew who I was.

"Come inside and tell me what it is you want," he said. I followed him through to his living room at the back of the house. The smell of toast hung in the air.

"Sit down then," Mr Beech removed a newspaper from the chair by the fire. He sat on an upright dining chair observing me from under bushy white eyebrows. I explained my problem as briefly as I could.

"Time for old Jimmy Jesus's birthday party again is it? I don't pay much heed to Christmas these days but I was an angel in the Sunday school play once," he barked with laughter, "that was a bad bit of casting but then our teacher was ever a foolish woman. Don't worry, Mrs Stratford, leave it to me. I may be old but I can answer the telephone and fetch you from the hall if needs be. Just let me know when I am to be stood down." He sketched a salute.

"Were you in the army?" I asked looking round the room for the usual photographs of young men in uniform. Only old calendars hung on the dingy wallpaper.

"Home Guard." He got up to open the drawer of a sideboard. "Bills, bills, bills," he muttered pulling out loose papers and crumpled brown envelopes. "Here," he handed me an old photograph, "you'll recognise a few faces on this." The village Home Guard grinned or scowled out of the picture according to their temperament. "There's me," Mr Beech stabbed a nicotine stained finger at his youthful image, "there's Harry Charles and Walt Ford, that's Bert, you've met him I know."

A youthful, Brylcreemed version of the diabetic who had landed on my hall floor gazed at me from the back row of the photograph. "Is that Mr Finch the sexton?" I peered at a familiar face, "and that looks like Mr Robbins. I post his letters sometimes."

"Yes that's them. We all get together at the British Legion meetings. It's the Christmas dinner tonight at The Crown," he pushed the photograph back into the drawer and crammed the bills in on top.

"You'll enjoy that?"

He shrugged, "well I don't cook much for myself and The Crown can do a turkey dinner." His tone dismissed any idea of a sentimental gathering. "There'll be a few less of us this year again," he gave me a wry smile, "us old men have a nasty habit of dying. Anyway, you go off and watch your children in the school play this afternoon, I'm glad to hear they still celebrate old Jimmy Jesus's birthday. Next thing you know some crack-pot will ban it!"

I got up to go, "I'll give you a ring when I'm ready to leave and put the answering machine on. Patients will be given your number to phone then and you can come to the hall and get me. I'll pop in when the play finishes. Then when we get back home I'll ring you again to say that I've got the 'phone back. Is that all right?"

He nodded, "orders understood," he opened the front door to let me out, "look at they old crows round the church tower."

I followed his gaze, a flock of black crows were wheeling round the weathervane and settling on the pinnacles of the tower.

"There'll be a funeral soon," Mr Beech said decisively, "the undertakers is about."

For a moment we watched the crows and I wondered what the outcome of the farm accident had been.

Peter did not come home at lunchtime so I guessed that his morning had been extra busy after his early call to Green Farm. At half past two I went to the dining room to tackle the answering machine which we stored under the sideboard. Dr Thomas had long since lost the instruction book but we had a few instructions scribbled in his prescription hand, on a piece of old surgery notepaper. I switched the machine on at the mains, crawled to the sideboard and knelt to twiddle the knobs. A light came on so I spoke into the microphone.

"Dr Stratford is out," I enunciated carefully, "in an emergency please telephone Northam 230 and leave a message." I changed the switches to test the tape. My own voice startled me. I checked the switches on the machine, got up from my knees and hoped that Mr Beech would be able to cope if there were any calls. I also hoped that his sense of humour would not upset any patients.

I arrived at the school hall with just enough time to help the children get dressed up. I pinned Clare into the blue robe she was to wear as Mary and swaddled the plastic doll.

The play was so short that it was over before I had time to concentrate my thoughts on the stage. The final tableau did catch my attention though. In front of the tall angels on the back row, the shepherds were grouped around a disguised tea chest full of straw in which Clare's doll was invisible. I made a mental note to remember not to call the doll Jimmy Jesus by mistake. James and the other two kings were engaged in a quiet game of push and shove which dislodged some of the 'jewels' from their crowns. I knew the 'jewels' were fruit gums glued to the cardboard crowns. The shepherds began to wield their crooks to hook the fruit gums to each other in hockey passes. The stage curtain fell as if the cords had been cut.

"She got that down fast," one of my neighbours said with a grin.

"Problem with the jewels in the crowns I think," I said. We all stood up as the clapping came to an end and the Mums prepared to face the battle backstage.

I emerged from the hall into the gloom of a December afternoon. We called round to see Mr Beech on our way home.

"You done Jimmy Jesus's birthday then?" he winked at the children who grinned with delight. "No telephone calls," he reported, "so you can scoot on home and turn that machine of yours off now." I thanked him profusely but he flapped an impatient hand. "go on with you, I didn't do anything. Any time you want help again just ask."

We had not been back in the house long before I saw Peter's car bounce into the drive. It was splattered with mud like a rally car. The children, still in their costumes, were eating biscuits at the kitchen table. Peter appeared carrying shoes caked with mud. I flung a newspaper down on the back door mat where he deposited his shoes.

"Guess what Daddy, the shepherds ate the jewels off our crowns," James said through a mouthful of biscuits.

"That's nice," Peter answered vaguely.

"No it wasn't," James was indignant.

"I need to change my trousers before evening surgery," Peter muttered. I saw that his knees were smeared with mud. He went upstairs and I followed him. "A farm worker was killed in the accident at Green Farm," he told me as he sat on the bed to pull off his muddy trousers. "They think his coat must have got caught in the PTO -"

"What's a PTO?" I took his dirty trousers and bundled them up for the wash. "Why don't you have a quick bath," I added, "you look cold as well as dirty."

"No time," Peter stood up, looked at his watch and then took the clean trousers I had pulled from the cupboard. As he struggled into them he explained, "the power take-off on a tractor is a moving bar to connect the tractor engine with another piece of equipment which needs power to run it." He fastened his belt.

"So if the farm worker's coat got caught in this PTO -?" I stared horrified by what I was imagining.

"He was either strangled or his neck was broken," Peter said tersely. "I leave that for the coroner to decide. It was a bit academic kneeling in the frozen mud trying to find signs of life."

"You'll have to scrub your nails," I said, catching sight of his hands.

Peter headed for the bathroom, "I did have a bit of a wash-up in the farmhouse," he scrubbed his nails hard with a nail brush scattering muddy splashes all over the basin and the splashback. He frowned at himself in the mirror, "what was James on about downstairs?"

"The School Nativity Play," I sat on the edge of the bath. Peter managed half a smile, "thank God for ordinary life. See you later." He hurried out of the bathroom and down the stairs. I heard the car roar up the lane as I cleaned the mud from the tiles and sluiced the hand basin. I took the trousers downstairs and put them in a bucket of water to soak. Outside the kitchen window the last light made a dark cut-out pattern of the village roofs and the pinnacled outline of the church tower. Smoke began to rise from chimneys. As I dried my hands I thought that I would light the fire for Peter to come home to after surgery.

I went out to the shed to fill the log basket. It was cold in the garden; there was a smell of frost in the air. I pulled logs from the pile in the shed and tumbled them into the log basket. As I carried the basket back towards the open back door I shivered and thought of the man who had been working alone in that muddy field and whom no fire would ever warm now.

Peter slept most of the evening in his chair by the fire. I felt curiously lonely watching him. Then as I was about to wake him and persuade him to go upstairs to bed the telephone rang. Peter stumbled out into the hall to answer it. I picked up our empty coffee cups and the newspapers as I heard Peter say, "OK I'll come."

"What is it this time?" I asked as I passed him in the hall pulling on his coat. He looked bleary-eyed.

"Don't know, sounds like a child with measles." He scribbled the number down on the telephone pad, "you go on to bed, Annie, I shouldn't be long."

He was out long enough for me to have fallen asleep. I soon woke up when he crawled into bed beside me.

"It's like having a snowman get into bed," I grumbled as I turned over and pulled the blankets around my ears. Peter's cold body had taken all the warmth. Soon he began to warm up and I tried to get back to sleep but Peter kept turning over restlessly.

"Stop scratching Peter," I dug him in the ribs. "What is the matter with you. Keep still, it's nearly midnight and I want to go to sleep."

"So do I, Peter sat up and snapped on the light.

I shaded my eyes, "now what's the matter?"

"I think I've picked up fleas," he examined his arms and legs, "the child I went to see didn't have measles at all, he was covered in flea bites and I think his little friends hopped off on to me!" He leapt out of bed and went to the bathroom where I heard him running a bath. The gurgling of the water tank woke the children. I crawled wearily out of bed to go and tuck them up again. From the bathroom I heard Peter shout "Got you!

"Peter," I remonstrated in a whisper from the bathroom doorway, "you've already woken the children once. I've just got them settled again so keep your voice down."

"I caught them look," triumphantly he held out the soap dotted with small black bodies pressed into the scented pink bar.

Suddenly I began to giggle. "You do look funny," I leaned helplessly against the door to watch Peter hunting through the forests of his body hair for fleas.

"What a day," I whispered, "Jimmy Jesus's birthday celebrations, death in a muddy field and now the great flea hunt."

Peter looked up from his search, "what did you call the nativity play?"

"It's what Mr Beech called it, he wasn't being really irreverent, just a bit eccentric I think. Oh I never told you about him did I? There hasn't been time." I threw Peter a clean towel from the airing cupboard, "you forgot to ask Joan to "phone-sit while I went to see the Nativity play. So I used the answering machine. The old gentleman who lives next door to the school let me put his number on the machine and promised to come for me if there was an urgent message.

"Sorry, I forgot all about the School play." Peter tied the towel round his waist. He was about to pull the plug when he said, "you know I think we'd better put all my clothes in this water overnight, just in case any more of the fleas are nesting in them."

"These trousers were clean on at tea time," I muttered as I cast Peter's clothes into the soapy bath water. We left them to sink, drowning any more unwanted visitors. As we went back to our cold bed the church clock struck midnight.

On Christmas Eve I began to feel like an over-wound clockwork toy as I rushed about with my head full of lists. There were presents to pack, beds to make up in the spare room for the family gathering and, of course, the marathon cook-up. At five o'clock on Christmas Eve I was at the kitchen sink peeling a bowlful of potatoes to be roasted with the turkey. The children were being entertained in the sitting room by visiting grandparents and Peter was still doing the last, pre-Christmas surgery. I glared at my reflection in the dark window behind the sink. "Why can't I sit by the fire with a glass of something warming?" I grumbled. A movement in the dark caught my eye. Startled, I dropped the potato I was peeling. A man stood outside the window, holding up a bleeding hand. The vegetable knife fell from my fingers into the muddy water as I gaped at the apparition. Then I realised, with relief, that I was not seeing a Christmas ghost but Tommy, Mr Bailey's elderly farm lad whom I had last seen herding the comical pig. I reached across the sink to open the window. Icy air rushed in.

"I don't suppose the doctor's about is he?" Tommy said laconically. "I've been and cut meself."

"Doctor's still doing surgery Tommy," I said, "But come round to the door so that I can wrap that hand up and telephone the surgery."

He pulled a grubby handkerchief from the pocket of his farm overalls, "no don't you bother," he wrapped his hand in a rag that looked as if it could have been used under a tractor bonnet. He raised his hand, now wrapped in the oily rag, "there see, he'll be all right "till I gets to the surgery. Thank you and a Merry Christmas." He melted into the darkness as I shouted after him, "hang on let me telephone and tell Doctor to wait for you." But I knew I was too late when I heard the roar of Tommy's motorbike engine. I wiped my wet hands hastily and went to telephone the surgery.

Peter answered, "I was just about to put the 'phone through to you and come home. I'm starving. What's for supper?."

I thought about the pile of potatoes for Christmas Day still waiting to be peeled, the stuffing to be made and was tempted to say 'bread and cheese,' but he still had work to do so I told him about the casserole in the oven before I explained about the ghostly figure at the window.

"OK," he said wearily," I'll stay here until Tommy arrives to be stitched up. Keep my supper warm."

As I put the telephone down I heard noises outside the front door, shuffling feet and coughs. "Now what?" I muttered angrily as I flung the door open to confront a startled band of church carol singers with torches and song sheets. For a moment their voices faltered on first line of 'The Holly and The Ivy,' then, as the family came out to the hall to listen with me, they began to sing cheerfully. Peter came home in time to hear them sing 'We Wish You A Merry Christmas,' and rattle their tin at him. He dug in his pocket and fed coins into the collecting tin as we all called out "Goodnight, Merry Christmas." The singers turned to walk down the lane, their breath smoking in the cold air.

"Something smells good," Peter came into the kitchen sniffing hungrily.

"Did you stitch Tommy's hand? You were very quick." I started to lay the table.

"Nope," Peter flung his coat on the back of his chair, "he'd cut a tendon so I've sent him off to the District General."

"Not on that old motorbike on a night like this I hope?"

Peter crouched down to peer into the oven, "of course not. I phoned his boss and Mr Bailey arrived to drive him to Casualty. They won't be back much before midnight I should think. Casualty on Christmas Eve will be mayhem."

I pictured gentle Mr Bailey and Tommy sitting with the Christmas drunks, "go and talk to your parents," I gave Peter a push towards the sitting room. "I'll get the supper on the table, it's you they want to see. Go on."

Later, after we had eaten, we were all enjoying a cup of coffee by the fire when the doorbell rang.

"Leave those," Peter said to the children who were examining the pile of presents under the Christmas tree in the corner of the room, "bedtime, go on."

"Ooh, must we?" they protested in chorus. I got up to shoo them upstairs as Peter opened the front door. From the landing I heard a breathless child's voice.

"Me Mum sent me. You know that perscription you give her this morning? Well me brother's gone and put it on the fire by mistake. She says the chemist's shut now so can she have some of your pills?" I heard no more as I ran bath water for the children. When I came downstairs Peter explained the problem to me while his sherry-flushed parents slept by the fire.

"It was a prescription for the contraceptive pill that went up in flames," Peter whispered, "the patient has seven children already so I hadn't the heart to make her wait for her prescription until the day after Boxing Day or there might have been an eighth child by September. I sent a sample packet of pills to tide her over the Christmas season!"

I sat down on the sofa beside him and stared into the fire. A choir on the radio were singing 'Once In Royal David's City.' When they got to "Where a mother laid her baby," I began to laugh.

"What's funny?" Peter turned to see what was amusing me.

"It's general practice," I gasped, "you never know what to expect next!"

Peter stretched his legs out to the fire, "To be really traditional I suppose I should be doing a home delivery at midnight, or at least delivering a baby at the maternity unit, not doling out contraceptive pills. Oh well," he raised the sherry glass in his hand, "Merry Christmas!"

# *Snowbound*

NOT LONG AFTER CHRISTMAS SNOW began to fall, at first silently then, as the wind rose, we found ourselves in the middle of a blizzard.

"Have you seen the way the wind is piling the snow outside?" Peter called me to the window on a Saturday afternoon in January. In the failing light we both stared out at the snow blowing horizontally across the field.

I looked at the field gate, just visible through the falling snow, "the lane will soon be filled with snow to the top of the walls.

Peter leaned on the windowsill, "at this rate I will never get the car out in the morning."

"And if you can't get out onto the road will the district nurses get out either?"

We looked at each other. The same idea struck us at the same time, "the diabetics!" Peter exclaimed, "someone has got to get to them with their insulin injections. If the worst come to the worst I'll have to get round on foot in the morning."

"What a good job you filled the Eastcombe box before the holiday," I shivered, "let's pull the curtains, there's nothing to be done tonight." The Eastcombe box had been handed down to us by Dr Thomas. Into the box, at the start of each winter, went a selection of emergency drugs. If Eastcombe was cut off, patients in difficulty could telephone Peter who would then advise them to go to the box and take out whatever tablets he recommended. The box was held at the pub where Peter did his weekly branch surgery.

"Jenny could always get out to see to any Eastcombe folk if I can't get up there," Peter said, naming the retired nurse who lived next door to the pub. Jenny could be relied on in an emergency. "What worries me isn't the people in the villages and hamlets but those in the remote farms and houses."

It was to be one of our most isolated patients who ran into trouble first.

When we got up on Sunday morning we found that the landscape had changed overnight.

"Look at this," Peter exclaimed as he pulled back our bedroom curtains. Shivering in my dressing gown I looked over his shoulder at the wintery scene.

"The greenhouse has almost vanished!" One corner of the greenhouse roof stuck out of a mound of snow.

"Look at the field wall," Peter pointed. "You could walk right over into the next field without knowing there was a wall there." Peter turned and began to pull on an assortment of old warm clothes. "This is going to be an interesting day," he said with relish.

I laughed, "trust you to enjoy it. I reckon you only chose medicine because you get a buzz from emergencies." As I dressed myself in layers of clothes I had to admit to myself that I found the snow exciting.

"The novelty will soon wear off," Peter said in his usual down-to earth way, "the first thing to do is to stop the children plunging into snowdrifts."

At breakfast it was even difficult to keep them still long enough to eat they were so excited.

"Can we get the sledge out?" James demanded as I stirred a pan of porridge. Before I could answer, the kitchen lights wavered and then went off. The porridge bubbled like lava and then subsided as the electric ring cooled beneath the pan.

"It's a power cut," said Peter, stating the obvious. He got up to light one of the candles we had left ready the night before and placed the candle in a jam jar in the centre of the table. I put bowls of hot porridge in front of the children who had stopped demanding to go outside but sat, big-eyed, staring at the candle. Peter made patterns in his porridge with brown sugar. "I'd better go out as soon as I've eaten this and see what the roads look like." His boots stood ready on the doormat beside the boxes of logs and buckets of coal he had brought in from the shed on Saturday. Before he had had time to finish his breakfast the telephone began to ring.

"That was the duty district nurse," he said when he sat down again, "she can't get her car out – she telephoned the local police who told her that all roads into the village are blocked. We are cut off!"

"Wow!" James breathed in awe.

"It won't be much fun if we run out of food," I told him.

"Are we likely to?" Peter looked at me in surprise.

"Well not for a long time," I had to admit, "but the selection could get a bit boring and we'll run out of bread and milk quickly."

"I wonder what the farmers will do if the milk tankers can't get through to collect the milk?" Peter got up from the table, "I suppose I could carry a squash bottle or something with me if I get called to any of the farms. They might be glad to let us have some – they'll have hundreds of gallons going to waste."

"I do hope there's nobody out there in real trouble," I said, staring out of the kitchen window. Light was beginning to creep reluctantly over the rim of the hills to illuminate a bleak landscape. The phone rang again, "I'll get it, Peter went out into the hall, and as I cleared the table I heard him say, "Alright, I'll have to come on foot so I don't know how long it will take me but I will come."

He came back into the kitchen in his anorak carrying an old rucksack which he began to fill from his Doctor's bag. "Sounds like a stroke out at Marsh End."

"But that's miles," I said, staring at the white wasteland outside the window.

"Well I'll have to go," Peter pulled on his boots, "the patient's husband is virtually blind so there is no way he can be left to cope. Now what," he exclaimed as there was a hammering on the front door. I followed him into the hall.

"Morning, Doc," Mr Finch's cheerful voice shouted from under a woolly cap, "we've come to ask you who wants digging out?"

I looked over Peter's shoulder and saw a group of men, fat with layers of clothes, carrying shovels and spades over their shoulders. "Looks like you're off somewhere already," Mr Finch observed, "can we help?" I saw that many of the men were ex-Home Guard members who looked as if they were enjoying a revival of the wartime spirit but I guessed that Peter had doubts about how fit they were for trekking in the snow or digging in the cold.

"Well … " he was obviously reluctant to damp their neighbourly spirit, "how about digging the path to the wardened bungalows? But take it slowly, the last thing I want is one of you chaps doing your backs in."

Or having a heart attack, I thought.

"Right you are doctor," Mr Finch turned round, "the old folks" bungalows it is. If you want any more help just give me a ring and I'll get this squad out again." Shouldering their spades the men set off down the lane.

"I almost expected them to go off singing "Hi ho, hi ho, its off to work we go," Peter said with a grin. "Good of them to offer though. He pulled up his anorak hood as he stepped out of the door into the knee deep snow. "Right then, I'm off to Marsh End. I'll call in and do the insulins on my way back but this visit has to come first. If any of the diabetics rings in a panic explain that I will get to them. Otherwise just hold the fort until I get back." He looked up at the sky. "You know if we get more snow the telephone lines will be the next thing to go."

I watched as he trudged off down the lane in the direction of Marsh End, such a short distance in a car but so long on foot in difficult conditions. I closed the door reflecting how much we take for granted in our world of cars, electricity, telephones and constant food supplies.

While I laid a fire I let the children play out in the garden. Blades of grass showed through the snow on part of the lawn where the wind had swept the snow up to form high banks against the garden walls. I could hear the children shouting and screaming with delight as they flung snowballs at each other. Then I heard something else - a tractor engine. I ran to the kitchen window just as James came to the door calling and pointing across the field to where a tractor pulled a trailer loaded with milk churns across the field path. At the wheel of the tractor sat Tommy, driving with his bandaged hand. He stopped the tractor level with our garden wall. I pulled on a coat and ran over the snow to speak to him.

"Mornin', Mrs Stratford," he said as if it were an ordinary day, "boss asked me to take these churns to the shop. The tanker cant get through and we don't want to pour good milk away. Lucky we kept an old churn or two. Do you want some milk?"

"Yes please. Hang on, Tommy," I ran back to the house to fetch two jugs. Tommy jumped up on the trailer, opened a churn and dipped my jugs in.

"Tell Mr Bailey I'll bring the money round when I can," I shouted as Tommy got back into the tractor cab. He shook his head, "boss told me he don't want no money for what we'd have to throw away. Better people should use it. I'll be back this way tomorrow, that is if the snow don't cover this path in the night. Funny old way the wind picks this dry snow up from some places then puts it down in heaps."

My gloved fingers felt as if they were already frozen to the jug handles. "Thank you Tommy and thank Mr Bailey for me please." I called as he turned the tractor ignition key.

"Bye, Tommy." The children waved wildly as the tractor bounced away along the field path. I stood for a moment watching as the swaying trailer grew smaller, looking like a toy in the expanse of white field.

It was lunch-time before Peter came back up the path. He was wet and cold but excited. "I had a lift on a JCB after I'd had to get a helicopter to take the patient to hospital," he told me when he stood on the doormat to pull his

G.Younger

boots off. "The old lady had had a stroke all right," he went on, "she was deeply unconscious. Her husband couldn't have been left to look after her. Come to that he needed looking after too. I phoned ambulance control who told me that they can't get any vehicles out on the road today. So, it was a helicopter or nothing." He sat down at the kitchen table. I handed him the cup of soup I had heated on our camping stove. James and Clare came in and stood on the doormat. I helped them out of their wet boots and took their snow-caked mittens off.

"How did the helicopter know which house to come to Daddy?" James asked wriggling with excitement as I tried to unzip his coat.

"I had to put out a marker," Peter cupped his cold hands around the mug of soup, "I took the old lady's bedspread out into the field near the cottage and weighed it down with stones. Then I saw the helicopter coming over the hill."

"Oh I wish I could have been there," James breathed, "a real helicopter."

"Did it land on the bedspread?" Clare climbed on a kitchen chair to sit next to Peter.

"Not quite," he smiled ,"but very near."

"What happened next?"

"Two men jumped out with a canvas stretcher and we went to the patient's house where she was wrapped up in blankets ready for the journey."

"Did her husband go with her?" I couldn't imagine the feelings of a blind husband only able to hear the commotion of his wife's leaving under such dramatic circumstances. Peter nodded, "yes I persuaded them to take him as well. He needed to be looked after too so I sent them together. If the hospital care to argue they can arrange to get him back." He grinned. "I think he will sleep in a warm bed tonight."

"And his wife?"

"Ah," Peter pulled a face, "I didn't like the look of her, I don't fancy her chances but at least she's in good hands now, not lying in that cold bedroom." I let the children take their mugs of soup into the sitting room by the fire. "The poor woman was lying in wet sheets in a freezing room," Peter confided when they were out of earshot. "Her poor old husband didn't even know where the clean sheets were kept. She had obviously been the one who did everything."

I offered Peter a refill of soup. James reappeared at the kitchen door. " You didn't tell us about the JCB and we forgot to tell Daddy about the milk."

"So we did," I agreed.

Glad of a cheerful subject Peter explained, "I was just ready to start back across the field when a JCB trundled along the lane. The driver offered me a lift so I got in the cab. But even he could only get as far as Green Farm. After that the road was blocked. The JCB had to be left in the yard. I walked across the field path where the snow was not piled so high. In places the wind has left huge frozen waves of snow but in other places its swept the paths clean. I've never seen such amazing snow-sculptures."

I told Peter about our morning milk delivery over the garden wall. "so thanks to Tommy and Mr Bailey we can go on making porridge and hot drinks."

At the end of the afternoon I looked out of the window to watch the sun setting. "Come and look at the colour of the field snow," I said. The children left the fireside to scramble up onto the windowsill.

"The snow is pink!" Clare exclaimed, "if I painted pink snow at school no one would believe me."

I cuddled them both to keep warm, "you're right though, the snow is pink," I agreed as the sun sank before our eyes. Flame coloured clouds cast bright reflections on the snow. I shivered as the light vanished. "Let's put more logs on the fire shall we?" I pulled the curtains on the cold night.

The village was cut off for four days. Eventually a snow plough cleared a narrow path along the main road and a police Land Rover got through from Moreton, with loaves of bread for the shop and more insulin supplies for Peter. But the side roads remained dangerous for weeks. The novelty of the snow wore off leaving us permanently cold and short tempered as we all grew tired of being confined to the house. Brandy did not help. He hated the snow so much that his house-training broke down completely. In spite of the cat litter tray I placed by the back door he kept creeping behind the sofa in the warmest room.

"The cat's peed in here again!" Peter shouted indignantly time after time. "I can smell it. Fine doctor's house this is for patients to come to – perfumed with cats' pee!"

"I seem to spend my life with a mop and bucket," I complained as my temper began to fray.

Peter's helicopter patient died in hospital and the freezing weather claimed more than one life. Two people died in a stranded car on an isolated road and our own Mr Polkinhorne was found dead one morning outside his shop. He had been clearing the snow from the shop doorway.

"He must have had a coronary," Peter told me when he returned from the emergency call. "Old Mr Beech found him when he went out early with his dog. Gave him a nasty shock."

I remembered seeing a youthful Mr Polkinhorne on the photograph of the village Home Guard. "That will be quite a funeral I should think," I commented, "I'd better go."

Mr Polkinhorne's funeral took place on a bleak Friday morning. There was still packed ice on the roads, snow in the field ditches and under north-facing hedges, but a good number of hardy village people turned out for the funeral.

With the rest of the congregation I stood up as the vicar entered by the west door of the church intoning those resounding words of the burial service, "we brought nothing into this world, and it is certain we can carry nothing out". I was touched to see that the procession was headed by Mr Beech carrying the village British Legion flag. All through the service he stood to attention near the coffin with the flag lowered to the ground; when the bearers lifted the coffin to carry Mr Polkinhorne out of the church, Mr Beech raised the flag and marched in front. I walked out of the church with all the other mourners through the Legion guard of honour; Mr Finch, Old Walt Ford and other men of the village standing rigidly to attention. For once there was none of the usual muted gossiping outside the church when the hearse left for the cemetery – it was too cold. I walked across the road to join the crowd of mothers waiting for their children at the school gate.

"We had to stay in for afternoon playtime," James told me in disgust when he burst out of the school door trailing his coat and shoe bag. "There was a funeral," he confided," looking sideways at his sister who was kicking broken ice on puddles in the lane, "When I went to the loo I saw big black cars and lots of people, that's why we were kept in."

"I know," I said quietly, "it was Mr Polkinhorne's funeral, I went to it.

"What do you do at funerals?"

"Well, you sing some hymns and say some prayers … "

"Oh, is that all,"

"No," I said warily, "then Mr Polkinhorne was buried."

James looked thoughtful, "like we buried my hamster in the garden?"

"Yes," I agreed, waiting for more questions, but James had suddenly had enough of funerals, "can we make toast by the fire for tea?"

"With plum jam," Clare joined in.

"Yes of course you can," I smiled to myself, grateful for the matter-of-factness of young children. We ran home to keep warm as the January afternoon darkened to dusk. I spared a last thought for Mr Polkinhorne's coffin under its cold blanket of earth and felt glad to be able to light a fire and to eat toast and plum jam with my children.

The following weekend we were on duty, unable to go out, so I bought pounds of Seville oranges to make marmalade. On Saturday afternoon Peter and I sat at the kitchen table. I squeezed the oranges then passed the skins to him to be cut up.

"We've got a production line going here."

"Your surgical skills do come in useful sometimes," I agreed as he cut four segments of orange peel into thin slices. "It's not a bad occupation for a cold afternoon on call is it?" Then the doorbell rang.

"I'll go," Peter said with resignation, hastily wiping his hands on a damp cloth. I stopped squeezing oranges to listen to the loud voices in the hall, then went to the kitchen door with half an unsqueezed orange in my hand.

"He were just going for goal doctor when this bloody great forward went for him." There were loud noises of assent. I peeped into the hall to see what looked like an entire football team, their studded boots caked with football-field mud, jostling round Peter. I realised that blood was steadily dripping from one player's nose to add to the mess on my floor. I went back into the kitchen, put the orange down and began to fill a bucket with hot water. Peter put his head into the kitchen,

"Got any … " Silently I handed him a box of tissues. He looked over my shoulder at the bucket under the tap, "sorry," he whispered and disappeared.

"Oh don't worry," I muttered to myself, "I just love cleaning floors." I wished that the cleaner from my old ward was on hand. I added a squirt of detergent to the water, smiling as I remembered Mrs Mac. She was so fat that if you came on her from behind, when she was on her knees cleaning the ward floor, her buttocks looked like the heads of two boys fighting under a blanket. Not that any of us would have dared tell her so, she was a fierce Devonian, despite her name, and frequently threatened doctors and nurses with a raised fist and shouts of "You mess up my clean floor and I'll give 'ee a doughboy see if I don't."

"Oh come back Mrs Mac," I sighed, "all is forgiven." Mrs Mac had made the ward's parquet floor shine in spite of being pounded by visitors and staff.

"I wonder what Mrs Mac would have made of my orange lino tiles," I heaved the bucket from the sink when I heard the door close on calls of "thanks doc," and "cheerio then."

I went into the hall. "Sorry about the mess love," Peter crouched down to pick up some of the blood-soaked tissues from the floor. He looked helplessly at the clods of mud and clumps of grass.

"They don't tell you about this sort of thing in those happy-ever-after doctor nurse romances," I said through gritted teeth. I began to swab the floor quoting in a falsetto voice, "He looked into her eyes which were like pools of blue beneath her starched lace cap," Peter bit his lip. I started to giggle, then we both began giggling like children at the mess all around us.

"If we'd done that you'd be cross," a voice from the landing made us look up. James and Clare both sat on the top step of the first flight of stairs looking down at us with disapproval. "You get cross if we come in with muddy shoes," Clare added self-righteously.

"I know," I wiped my eyes, "I'll just clean the floor then it's back to the orange squeezing"

"The footballers did ask if we were running a marmalade factory," Peter gasped and we started to laugh again.

After the excitement of the snow we had weeks of weather which turned the countryside into a place which town-dwellers, who dream of cottages, would do well to sample before moving to the country. Dark mornings led quickly to dark afternoons, unlit lanes were awash with mud from the wheels of tractors. Mud spread into the lanes from field gateways where vehicles and animals churned the soil. The joys of snow and the visual pleasures of hoar frost and sunsets were a memory lost in the gloom of February. The surgery waiting room was filled with patients coughing and sneezing.

I was buying toothpaste in the village chemist's shop one morning when I heard an angry voice at the counter.

"That new doctor says I've got to buy this cough mixture from you," the red-faced lady brandished a scrap of paper at Mr Phipps, our mild-mannered pharmacist. I shrank behind a display of face flannels. "I shall report him," she demonstrated her cough, "I pay my taxes like everybody else, I know my rights, I'm entitled to a prescription for my medicines." Her indignation irritated her chest again. When the eruptions had subsided Mr Phipps put a bottle on the counter. "This is the mixture that doctor has recommended for you."

The lady opened her purse reluctantly, "should be on prescription," she muttered, "how much is it?"

"Ninety pence," Mr Phipps said, adding blandly, " and as you know, for a prescription I would have to charge you one pound."

Scarlet-faced, the customer handed over a pound, coughing to cover her confusion.

When the door slammed behind her I took my toothpaste to the counter, "whew, I wonder if Peter had explained that he was trying to save her ten pence?"

Mr Phipps shook his head as he opened the till to take out my change, "I very much doubt if he got a word in between that lady's chronic cough and her equally chronic indignation!"

When Peter came home he was not in a mood to be entertained. "I got the car stuck in a muddy ditch at Eastcombe," he grumbled as he sat down to lunch, "and then I barked my shins when I eventually got to the house I'd been called to." He pulled up his muddy trousers to display a livid bruise on one shin.

"What on earth did you walk into?"

"A lawn-mower," he said, looking hopefully at the oven. I turned from the soup I was stirring, "a lawn-mower! Where was your patient, in a garden shed?"

"No, in an armchair in a rather cluttered cottage front room."

"And the lawn-mower?" I poured soup into two dishes.

"That was in the room too, right inside the front door," Peter inspected the soup I put in front of him.

"It's minestrone," I said defensively.

"Ah, left-over vegetable soup with pasta. I'm used to avoiding dogs, prams and old milk churns," Peter went on hastily, "but this was the first lawn mower I have encountered inside a house."

"Perhaps someone wanted to mow the carpet," I said facetiously, "was it a shag pile carpet?"

"Carpet, what carpet?" Peter stirred his soup, waiting for it to cool. "There are no carpets in that cottage just lino and a lot of dangerous loose rugs for the old couple to fall over. I never did find out why the lawn-mower was there. Most of them are stored in redundant privies. Mind you, my patient was fairly lucky to be alive."

"Go on," I could hear a story coming.

"The patient's wife is confused, gently demented really and he looks after her very well. But last night it was the old man who was ill. He got out of bed and left the bedroom saying that he felt cold. The old lady got up when he didn't return to bed and went to look for him. She found him unconscious in the airing cupboard!"

I choked on my soup, "well I suppose that's a good place to go to get warm. What happened next?"

"The old lady decided that he was probably dead and since it was the middle of the night there was nothing she could do about it she closed the door, left him propped up in the airing cupboard and pottered off to bed! This morning she had forgotten where he was. She really is rather a confused old lady." Peter scraped his dish and looked up at the saucepan.

"More left-over veg soup?" I asked. "Go on what next?"

"Well, luckily the old chap didn't die of hypothermia in the airing cupboard and by morning he recovered enough to get to the telephone and call the surgery. I think he may have had a tiny stroke. I sent him to the Cottage Hospital."

"And his poor wife?"

"Gone to their daughter in Moreton." Peter wiped round his dish with a piece of bread, "I've had unconscious patients in bathrooms and garden sheds but never in an airing cupboard before!"

The short dark afternoons deprived me of the walks I enjoyed so much. By the time Joan took over the telephone at half past four each day it was too dark to go out. My brief time of freedom during morning surgery always seemed to be filled with shopping or urgent jobs. I missed the light afternoons and I missed my village friends too. Mr & Mrs Hayward both had nasty coughs and were staying indoors; Mr Bailey's bad leg had confined him to the house so I was pleased when, one afternoon, Mr Finch came to the back door as I was ironing.

"I thought you might like one of these to brighten up your windowsill." Mr Finch put a pot plant down on the kitchen table, "I grows these Cinerarials every year." The shocking pink flowers clashed wonderfully with the orange lino tiles of the kitchen floor.

"Mr Finch it's a superb plant," I spoke the truth, "I've never see such huge flowers on a Cineraria." He smiled with pleasure, "Well I thought what with the mud and the rain and all you'd be about fed up with country life just now."

I shook my head, "not really, although I must admit I shall be glad to see the spring."

Mr Finch agreed, "If we lived in a town we would miss these gloomy days but then we wouldn't be on hand when the sun comes back with the primroses would we?" I put the kettle on to make Mr Finch a cup of tea. As I filled the kettle I looked out at the darkening garden and realised that in a very short time we were going to experience our first country springtime.

## Full Circle

BEFORE SPRING CAME TO THE village, winter played a short encore. The roads were ice-glazed and new leaves edged with a fringe of ice crystals. I played truant one sparkling morning after I had taken the children to school when I walked out to the ford. There I leaned over the handrail of the footbridge. Spray from the stream had settled on the pendant brambles overnight and the layers of ice had formed into icicle chandeliers. On the bare branches of the hedge I found Blackthorn buds and one or two open flowers, lacy as a bridal veil.

"Real blackthorn winter this is, Mrs Stratford," Mr Bailey called from his kitchen door as I passed by his yard.

"How good to see you about again, Mr Bailey," I crossed the yard to talk to him. Strong sunshine had melted ice on the yard puddles turning them to what Mr Bailey always called gravy. I was wearing wellies so the brown liquid under the ice-patterns didn't deter me.

"How are you?" I asked when I reached his door.

"There's nothing been wrong with me," Mr Bailey emphasised, "just this bally old leg. Here you come in and see my Easter lilies." He stood back to let me into the lean-to greenhouse by the kitchen door. Inside, the shelves were full of plants; there were seed trays green with sprouting seedlings, polyanthus flowering in small clay pots and hyacinths in old chamber pots. "Here they are," Mr Bailey showed me a row of stately-home sized clay pots bursting with dark green leaves. He parted the leaves of the nearest one, "there's a bud right down in the heart look," I peered and saw a knuckle of lily bud pushing upwards. "I always have a dozen or so blooms ready for the flower ladies to arrange on the altar at Easter," Mr Bailey said proudly.

"It does smell lovely in here, Mr Bailey," I took a deep smell of air rich with the smell of damp earth and hyacinths. Outside, in spite of the sun, the air was still frosty; in Mr Bailey's greenhouse it was perpetual spring.

As I walked back towards the footbridge, reluctant to return to housework and typing, Tommy's tractor roared down the lane. He drove into the ford and stopped.

"Got water in the engine Tommy?" I shouted from the bridge.

"He grinned, "no, boss wants I to clean th'old tractor up a bit. This is the quickest way." He reached a bald broom from his trailer and began to scrub the tractor wheels with it. Mrs Bailey's ducks quacked indignantly as the stream turned dark brown. They waddled out to the grassy patch under the hedge.

"You're making Mrs Bailey's nice white ducks dirty," I called.

"Stupid birds," he looked at the Aylesbury ducks, "they needs a drake to keep they in order." He pushed his broom back onto the trailor and walked over to the bridge where he stood just below me, the water swirling round his boots." My daughter's got a drake with nothing better to do than make a mess of her garden. He were a pet for her kids nice little fluffy duckling he were but he've turned into a randy drake. Reckon I'll ask the missus if she wants a new drake for them ducks."

"What happened to Mrs Bailey's drake?"

"Fox got him," Tommy said laconically. "Well, must get on, Cheerio." He climbed back into his tractor cab, started the engine and caused a tidal wave of water as he drove out of the ford towards the farmyard. I watched until the water stopped swirling, the ducks returned and my ears began to ache with the cold. I walked towards the lane where puddles glittered in the sun and thoughts of Easter lilies and ducklings made spring seem a reality.

"Can I go and help make the Mothering Sunday posies at the vicarage on Saturday?" I asked Peter one March morning. "The vicar's wife telephoned and asked me for flowers and help. I would quite like to and I'd like to get to the service on Sunday."

Peter sighed. He was looking very harassed after a long winter of continuous work. "We are on duty on Sunday."

"Could you ask Dr Thomas to help?"

"He's away somewhere sunny," Peter said with a touch of envy in his voice.

"Well shall I ask Mr Beech? I'm sure he would come to the vicarage or the church to get me if you had a real emergency." Peter's face cleared, "if you don't expect me to come to the service I suppose that would work."

"Any excuse to get out of church? OK," I changed tack hastily, "leave it to me, I'll ask Mr Beech."

I made the same arrangements as before and after lunch on Saturday I went into the garden to look for suitable posy flowers. The snowdrops were over and the daffodils too big for posy making but I found a few pink and blue lungwort flowers by the old shed and some primulas under the wall so I had a respectable basketful with plenty of greenery added.

When I arrived at the vicarage there was a note pinned to the front door which simply said WALK IN. I pushed the half-open door and stepped inside. A smelly paraffin heater, standing on acres of Victorian tiles, failed to add any heat to the hall. I could hear voices through an open door beyond the staircase. I caught a glimpse of a long landing and a row of bedroom doors with a pile of dirty washing outside each door. I wondered what glimpses of our lives patients who called at the cottage took away with them.

The voices and a lingering smell of food guided me to the vicarage kitchen.

"Ah, Mrs Stratford, do come in and join us dear." Mrs Straker stood at the head of a table. Two antique china wash-stand bowls full of flowers and leaves stood in the centre of the long table. The group of ladies, busy making posies, looked up and May Hayward made a space for me beside her. I added my flowers and greenery to the nearest bowl. Miss Macdonald gave me a curt nod and I wondered if her snappy dog was still on Phenobarbitone. Mrs Bailey showed me how to bind a small bunch of flowers with raffia and I chose my first posy as the gossiping resumed.

"Aren't they pretty dear?" Emily Mundy whispered as I picked some small pale mauve iris flowers to add to my bunch.

"They are," I agreed, "like tiny furled silk parasols until they open. What are they called?"

"Oh don't ask me their name dear," Emily shook her head as she took an iris for her posy. "I just call them winter iris, they grow like weeds under my wall. If you want some I'll dig up a clump for you."

"Iris Stylosa, Mrs Stratford dear," Mrs Avery, the parish council chairman called down the table, "if you want to grow them don't coddle them," she sniffed like a grandmother whose grandchildren were in danger of being spoiled. "They thrive on neglect, plant them in poor soil, under a wall where there's plenty of rubble in the soil. Give them a rich diet and they won't flower for you."

"Now you know!" Mrs Bailey whispered to me with a wink.

"I love those antique bowls," I whispered back, "fancy using them for this job, most people would put the flowers in washing-up bowls.

"Oh those come out regularly," Mrs Bailey lowered her voice although the rest of the posy makers were busy discussing the problem of the village hall roof. "You must have seen the big bowl before Christmas. The vicar always brings it to church on stir-up Sunday full of pudding mixture which he gets the children to stir. One of the bowls will probably appear again at Easter, full of chocolate eggs for the children."

"Tea everyone?" Mrs Straker left the table to fill the large Aga kettle. I was just looking forward to a cup of tea when Mr Beech put his head round the kitchen door.

"You're wanted at home, Mrs Stratford, Doctor's been called out urgent. You'd better get on home too Emily, it's old Luke."

There were murmurs of consternation as Emily and I left our half finished posies on the table.

"You run on home dear," Emily said as we closed the vicarage door behind us, "your legs are younger than mine."

"I must be quick," I agreed, "or the telephone will be left unanswered. I ran along the High Street passing Emily's house where Peter's car stood by the gate. I wanted to go in and help but I had to get back home. As I ran I remembered Joan's habit of quoting Milton which I changed to "they also serve who only answer the phone".

"Daddy had to go," Clare greeted me at the door. I collapsed onto a kitchen chair to regain my breath. The telephone began to ring. James and Clare looked pleased that I was home to answer it. "Peter will have to get a bleep or a modern answering machine or something," I muttered as I went to pick up the phone, "I'm chained to this thing."

"Is he there?" The voice was that of our paranoid patient, Mrs Black.

I took a deep breath, "if you mean Doctor Stratford, no he has been called out to an emergency." I knew that I sounded frosty.

"Well this is an emergency too," came the predictable reply, "I need new elastic stockings. My legs are real bad. All the elastic's gone in the tops."

I closed my eyes and leaned against the wall. I tried not to picture Mrs Black's baggy stocking tops. "Go to the surgery on Monday morning and doctor will give you a note for new stockings."

"But me legs is terrible," the voice rose to panic pitch.

"Make yourself a cup of tea, Mrs Black, and go and sit down with your legs raised up on a cushion," I replied with all the patience I could muster. "Rest them as much as you can over the weekend." The phone went dead as she hung up. I went into the kitchen to make myself a cup of tea. Peter came back just in time to join me.

"Old Luke was unconscious in Emily's greenhouse," he said briefly when I poured his tea. "He survived the winter only to succumb now."

"Did he stay in that greenhouse in all that snow? Do you know, I never gave him a thought."

Peter shook his head and cupped his hands around the mug of tea. "Emily took him inside during the blizzard but he moved out as soon as the thaw came. He couldn't bear to be under a roof. There can't be many shell-shocked old soldiers left now." Peter sighed. "I tried to talk to him about it once. I think I had some daft idea about trying to get counselling for him but I was fifty years too late. He was in the trenches where, according to Emily, all his mates were killed around him. So he feels safe in the greenhouse where he can see the sky."

"What do you think happened today?"

"Probably a small heart attack. When Mr Finch popped in to see him, as he often does, he found Luke rolled up in blankets on his camp bed unconscious."

"Oh, I am glad Emily wasn't the one to find him, I said thinking of Emily Mundy's soft spot for old Luke. Will he be OK?"

Peter looked thoughtful, "he will probably pull through but not to come home to life in a greenhouse."

I felt an idea forming in my head. "Peter, what about the old caravan? You know Mrs Lee doesn't want to get rid of it and Sam wants it for scrap. Couldn't Luke live in there? Mrs Lee would just love to have an old soldier in her garden to fuss over. It would be a good use for the van."

Peter leaned back in his chair, "the old van isn't the warmest and most comfortable place to be in, as I know to my cost, but I supose it is a good deal better than the greenhouse. I'll ask Mrs Lee first. Sorry you had to come back from the vicarage by the way."

I poured more tea for us both, "no problem. We'd nearly finished anyway. Oh I did have one call while you were out. It was Mrs Black wanting new elastic stockings."

Peter groaned, "she's a menace."

"She's a sad case," I agreed, "I suppose you've tried luncheon club and …"

"Everything -" Peter said, "she doesn't want to know. I'll sort out her stockings on Monday. You go to the Mothering Sunday service tomorrow as planned. Our system with Mr Beech did work didn't it? I must ring and thank him."

I went to the Mothering Sunday service half expecting Mr Beech to come hurrying up the nave in search of me but this time there were no emergencies. I was able to enjoy watching the village children queue up to receive their posy from the vicar's china bowl. Clare and James each brought a dripping posy to me in the pew and I indulged in some unashamed maternal pride.

On the day before Good Friday Joan agreed to stay on late so that I could go shopping in Torminster. We were expecting our parents for the Easter weekend so I had a lot to get. I hurried along the High Street burdened with carrier bags full of shopping when I noticed people at the kerbside. My heart sank. If it's a road accident I'll have to help I thought, as I walked towards the edge of the crowd.

"They can break a man's leg you know," a voice called excitedly from the kerbside.

"They'll have to fetch the RSPCA."

"Or the Bishop. It belongs to him you know."

I craned my neck to see one of the swans from the Bishop's Palace moat standing on large flat feet in the centre of the road. A traffic-jam filled the High Street. Delivery drivers revved their engines and sounded their horns but the swan looked unmoved. A policeman appeared around the corner.

"About time too," someone said as the policeman stepped into the road with his arms outstretched under his black shoulder cape. A patrol-car officer in flat hat and jacket would not have looked half as impressive as the Bobby in cape and helmet.

"Come on sunshine," he shouted, "time to go back home." As he advanced the swan moved nervously, eyeing the policeman who looked like a big black-winged bird. To everyone's relief and amusement the swan began to waddle past the cars and lorries towards the market place and the moat.

Over lunch Peter told me an amusing story from the surgery after I had recounted the swan incident.

"I had an old farmer in today complaining about his backache. When I told him to be careful not to bend and twist at work, he said, "you try milking a herd of cows doctor, without bending and twisting when you have to bob up and down to keep out of the showers of shit!"

When we had stopped laughing Peter said, "oh Mrs Lee likes your idea about Luke living in the old van. Luke was transferred back to the Cottage Hospital today so Mr Finch is going to visit him and try to sell him the idea."

Mr Finch came to see me that afternoon. He settled down on a kitchen chair. "Well," I said eagerly, "how is Luke and will he live in the caravan?"

Mr Finch stroked his moustache, "he told me he'd always fancied a caravan but never had the money to buy one. He used to think he wanted to go out on the road, with a gipsy van and horse but he knows the days for that have past. He'll be Mrs Lee's lodger if she'll have him. Mind you," Mr Finch grinned, "she might have a party in her garden."

"Party?"

"Luke said if he comes back to the caravan he's going to celebrate and have all his old friends round. Old cronies like Bert and Alf with their bottles of scrumpy."

"Bert was my first patient," I remembered, "he fell in through the front door. Perhaps I should warn Mrs Lee. If Bert falls through the caravan door he could go straight through the floor, it's not very solid."

"I wouldn't worry, Ma Lee can sort out a few old men on the cider. You should have seen her husband and her sons. She'll have a new lease of life with all that action in her garden. She told me only last week that life in her bungalow was boring."

"Do you realise," Peter said later when he had finished his supper, "that we have been here a whole year today?"

"I'd forgotten the year is up today," I stroked Brandy who was kneading my knees with his claws, "the cat has certainly grown. He was just a kitten when Walt Ford brought him".

"I had forgotten until I wrote the date on the note for Mrs Black's elastic stockings." Peter grinned, "You know, with elastic stockings and escaped swans, showers of cow shit and patients convalescing in old caravans, I reckon you could write a book about life in country practice."

I looked thoughtfully at the old typewriter on the kitchen table as the phone began to ring.

"I'll get it," Peter got up from the table. I wondered what new story this phone call was going to bring. Then I heard the piercing voice as Peter held the receiver away from his ear.

"I'm going doctor, I'm dying, you must come quickly!"

"Mrs Pringle," Peter sighed, "at this rate you'll outlive me." There was a silence on the other end and I began to smile. The year had come full circle. Our seasons were marked, not by the weather or the flora and fauna of the countryside but by the repeating pattern of our patients and their problems. I reflected on the past year and stared speculatively at the typewriter.

❧ ❧ ❧ ❧ ❧